C000215085

Wiltshire S
of the
Supernatural

Sonia Smith

COUNTRYSIDE BOOKS
NEWBURY, BERKSHIRE

COUNTRYSIDE BOOKS
3 Catherine Road
Newbury, Berkshire

To view our complete range of books,
please visit us at
www.countrysidebooks.co.uk

ISBN 978 1 84674 037 4

Designed by Peter Davies, Nautilus Design

Produced through MRM Associates Ltd., Reading
Typeset by Mac Style, Nafferton, E. Yorkshire
Printed by Cambridge University Press

All material for the manufacture of this book was sourced from sustainable forests.

Contents

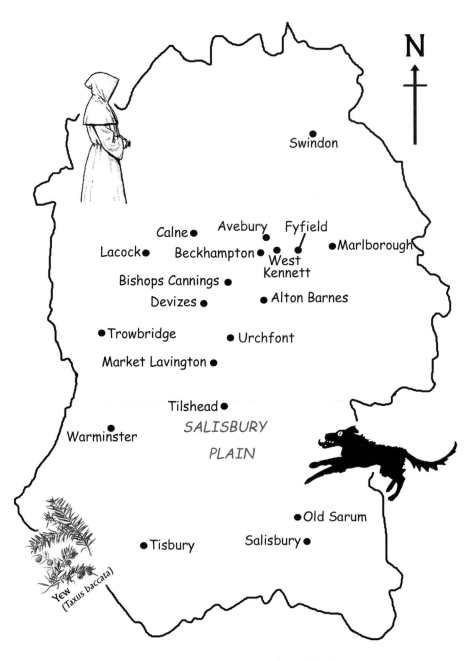

N

Swindon

Calne

Avebury   Fyfield

Lacock   Beckhampton   Marlborough
West
Kennett

Bishops Cannings

Devizes   Alton Barnes

Trowbridge   Urchfont

Market Lavington

Tilshead

SALISBURY

Warminster   PLAIN

Yew
(Taxus baccata)

Tisbury

Old Sarum

Salisbury

MAP OF WILTSHIRE

Introduction

Some of the ghost stories in this book were told to me by various people over the years, others are accounts of my own experiences, but they are all totally authentic and true. I am eternally grateful to everyone who shared their tales with me, and although they are too many to mention by name, they all have my heartfelt thanks.

I was born in a small village called Urchfont in Wiltshire. My family had always lived there. In fact, on my maternal grandmother's side, they had been in Wiltshire for generations. It was a time of simple living, and simple people. And by this I do not refer in any way to the intellect of those people, but rather to the lives that they led. We were indeed living in Tolkien's Hobbiton, or as near as it could be. I think I saw the last of it in my childhood, because by the time the 1970s had arrived, the village was already on the change. Modern life had come at last but luckily a lot of the old characters were still alive and they seemed to staunchly refuse to change with the times. Many people still hunted rabbits and nearly everyone grew their own vegetables in their ample gardens. People held simple religious beliefs; a few went to church, many did not. Superstitions were rife, and no one washed clothes on Good Friday, 'Lest the water turn to blood', or looked at a new moon through glass for fear of bad luck for that month.

People were closer to Nature than the Church. The Church was held in awe, but it wasn't something that they understood. Nature was something they could relate to. They watched the moon for signs of coming weather, and the way that animals behaved foretold coming events. The supernatural was something they lived with. They had no need to believe or disbelieve; it was just simply there.

Witches existed, but were not called witches; that is, unless they created havoc in the community, then they were known as witches in the blackest sense. But it was accepted that there were 'white witches', or wise women, who were asked for help with ailments, love potions, abortions, midwifery, the lifting of curses and cures for animals. They could often ease the passing over of the ill, and would lay out the dead. Not to mention their skill with divination, or fortune telling as it was known. Ghosts were a part of life too. Nearly everyone in the village had at one time in their life seen a ghost, or experienced a ghostly happening.

These stories were passed down from generation to generation. At times like Hallowe'en it was a favourite pastime to sit around an open fire, in a cosy cottage, and relate these tales to wide-eyed children. Some of them were told to me in just this way; others were related to me when I was a little older. So I decided to write them all down so that other people could enjoy them too. We are living in a different world; a world where there seems so little time for storytelling, more is the pity.

I hope that these stories will be told on dark winters' nights to today's wide-eyed children – and to their parents, too. For everyone loves a good tale, particularly if it happens to be true!

Sonia Smith

The Disembodied Hands

This is a story told to me by my mother. She said it was related to her by the then landlady of the Nag's Head public house in Urchfont.

The pub at that time, in the 1950s, that is, was a very simple affair. Inside there were bare floors, wooden benches and scrubbed heavy wooden tables. No jukebox or any other modern machine adorned the place; entertainment consisted of a singsong, or sometimes someone might bring in an accordion or fiddle and play a tune or two. Bread, cheese and pickles were available to eat, with big jugs of strong cider or beer to wash it all down. No one pulled a pint those days, the beverages were served at the tables from the big jugs. Ernie Allsop was the landlord who served the customers, and his wife Alice made the plates of bread and cheese for those who had ordered them for supper.

A cheery fire burned in the hearth in the bar whenever the weather turned cool; and often there was only the sound of the click of dominoes, the hushed voices of the players and the tick of the old grandfather clock that stood in the corner of the room and chimed occasionally with sonorous notes. Often later when the good ale had gone down, the male voices grew a little louder and a song or two might break out, or a story. No female voices much were heard; it was the fifties in the country, and country life was, as ever, way behind the more liberated ways of the city dwellers. A few women sometimes accompanied their husbands, and usually sat with other women for a gossip. Women never went to the pub alone, well at least the ones who considered themselves 'decent women' did not. Children were sometimes allowed in, that is if they went and sat quietly on one of the big wooden hard benches, or 'settles' as the locals called them. And quiet and well behaved they always were, swinging little legs too short to reach the ground from the settle, sipping Sunbright Lemonade.

Well Alice, the landlady, was a hard worker, as was her husband Ernie. But Alice had the bulk of the housework to do, both in their private rooms and in the pub itself. She was a tiny woman, but wiry, and she had an abundance of energy, even though her hair had by now turned white with age. She had to beat the rugs in the yard by hand, with a big stick to get the dust out. No vacuum cleaners or other 'gadgets' had yet reached the village, save perhaps to a few of the wealthy there, so housework was hard work. She also had to sweep the floors clean with a broom and polish all of the settles and other woodwork by hand with turpentine and beeswax. Then, of course, there was the washing up to do, all of it. So many glasses, beer tankards and plates! All done in the old Belfast sink in the kitchen. Finally, the glasses had to be dried and polished before opening time in the evening.

One bright morning in late summer, after Alice had finished her usual housework in the bar, she went through to the kitchen only to find an absolute mountain of washing up to be done. There had been quite a party in the pub the night before; a friend of Ernie's was celebrating the birth of his first grandchild with his local cronies. Everyone had stayed rather late at Ernie's invitation. Alice had gone up to bed and left the men to it. But she had not slept well with all of the noise coming up from the bar. So today she was quite exhausted after her usual work, and the huge pile of washing up was more daunting than it usually seemed.

Ernie had gone off early to collect some goods from the nearby town of Devizes, so Alice was completely alone. She looked at the washing up and almost burst into tears, not really like her, but it had been a busy week and she certainly wasn't getting any younger. Pulling herself together she rolled up her sleeves, went over to the sink, and started to fill it with water from the geyser. She was about to immerse her poor red, rough hands when something happened that made her nearly faint. In fact, she later said about the incident, 'I thought I were a-going to drop down daid!'

A pair of hands appeared, resting on the edge of the sink, *disembodied hands.* They were beautiful, white and long fingered, the hands of a woman. Then, to Alice's great surprise, they began to wash up the glasses, carefully putting them on the drainer to dry. Alice, dumbfounded, watched as the hands worked deftly and quickly, until the whole mountain of washing up had disappeared!

Alice could hardly believe that this had happened, she was of a practical nature and not given to fantasy of any kind, and she had never experienced anything remotely like it before in her life. But she had seen this with her own eyes. She told my mother that this happened several times more in her lifetime as landlady of the Nag's Head. The 'Helping Hands', as Alice called them, always seemed to appear when there was almost too much washing up for her to cope with, or when she was unwell.

'They was angel's hands,' Alice told my mother. And who are we to disagree with her?

Smashed Teacups

When I was a child in the early 1960s, Urchfont village was very much the same as it had been for centuries. But the march of time was fast travelling our way. There was talk of widening the road through part of the village. Everyone who lived on the edge of this small road was astounded at the very thought of it.

We children would stand on the high bank overlooking the narrow little road, eagerly waiting for the arrival of a motor vehicle. One or two a day would happen by, and often we would wave and cheer, especially if it was an army lorry full of soldiers, heading for Salisbury Plain. And the soldiers of course would all wave back to us, making us cheer the more. But more likely than not, to our disappointment, it would be an old open topped tractor rumbling along, with old Tom in it, red face beaming at us, to go and get the cows in for milking.

So no one understood why the road had to be widened at all, and the thought of it displeased most villagers, and it certainly displeased those who would lose a good part of their front gardens for it. Change wasn't that welcome, but it came anyway. Consumer society had reached the countryside. Ordinary people suddenly wanted to look like movie stars, and it became quite a status symbol to own a car.

But some people held firmly to the past, and would not let go for anything. Such a one was Rachel Merris. Rachel lived in a small thatched cottage not far from the village green, with her only living relative, her brother, who was fondly known in the village as 'Tink'. She also owned eight rather fine cats of differing colours, ages and sex. Rachel was a very old woman in the 1960s, and, for some reason only beknown to her, she wore clothes that looked like they were about 50 years out of date, and these clothes were always black in colour.

Whether it was for this reason, or the fact that she liked occasionally to help sick people and animals, using home-made herbal potions, people thought that she might be a witch, though it may be said that some just thought her rather mad, the more kindly among them calling her eccentric. Most of the village children, and indeed some of the adults, were in awe of her. This was a good thing for Rachel as she led a very peaceful life, tending to her lovely garden, feeding and petting her cats, and sitting in her big quiet kitchen, with only the ticking of a clock or a kettle singing in the hearth to bother her.

Well, one day in the school summer holidays, when all of us children were looking for new and exciting things to do, it was suggested by one of our number that we should go and find out if Rachel Merris was really a witch. We were all excited, and all rather frightened, although of course we did not admit to being afraid. We had to toss a coin as to which of us would go, and it was decided out of the seven of us, three would go. We were, of course, far too scared for anyone to go alone.

And so it turned out that it was me, my cousin Richard and another friend of ours, Rodney, that were the ones to go on this dangerous mission of finding out about witches.

With pounding hearts and sweating palms, we walked up the narrow little path leading to Rachel's back door. The other children watched us go, all wide-eyed; they screamed with laughter, to relieve the tension that everyone was feeling more than anything else. Tall foxgloves and hollyhocks lined the way as we walked on toward the cottage. The path had been made of the cold cinders emptied from the fireplaces. It was a warm day, and no sound came from the cottage as we approached. Huge black and yellow bumblebees buzzed and alighted to sip nectar from deep inside the foxglove flowers.

It was, in fact, so still and peaceful and sleepy, that it gave Richard the opportunity he had been looking for, and he quickly said, 'No one at 'ome. Le's go!'

But Rachel must have heard him, because she appeared at the back door, a gaunt and sombre figure in black against the background of colourful red geraniums that stood in abundance both sides of her doorway. 'What is it you childer want?' she asked, not unkindly. But her presence had made our knees go weak.

The boys were now really ready to run, so thinking we must seize the opportunity, or miss our mission, I spoke up quickly, 'We've come to see yer cats.'

The boys looked as if their boots had been glued to the spot, although it was evident they longed to run away. They both gave me a quick glance that definitely said 'You are mad!'

'Well, if's the cats you want to see, you'd better come in,' Rachel said to us all, her face expressionless.

'Come on then!' I said, pushing the boys in front of me, in case they decided to turn tail.

We found ourselves in a warm bright kitchen, although the windows were rather small, and only let in a little of the dazzling sunlight. There was a fire alight in an old iron range; the range carefully blackened and leaded. A kettle sat on top, and a huge stew-pot. A brace of rabbits were in the corner ready to be skinned and dressed for the table. We did not think dead animals macabre in any way, as we were all used to the sight of them.

There was the usual settle by the hearth, and an old scrubbed wooden table, and an odd assortment of clumsy wooden chairs and stools. All of the seating was covered in patchwork cushions of the most gorgeous colours and designs. A tall, glass fronted clock with a pendulum ticked harmoniously on the wall. Everything was spotlessly clean. Geraniums were on all of the window-sills, bursting with colour.

And everywhere there seemed to be cats. Cats of all colours and sizes. Three marmalade kittens played together with an old blue ball of wool on the floor. Two fat tabbies dozed on the deep window-sills amongst the geraniums. Two were asleep on the cushions of the settle, one upside down, legs asprawl, in cat abandonment.

'I'll get you a sweet each,' said Rachel, opening a door that seemed to lead to a dark passageway.

We held our breath as she left. Dark thoughts ran through our heads. What would she do? Did witches eat children, or sacrifice them? I remembered reading in my father's newspaper about some man they called 'The Beast', Aleister Crowley by name, who claimed to sacrifice children. He had something to do with witchcraft! I could see the boys were very edgy, and wanted to just run out and away.

When it happened, we had no idea what it was. We heard a thud, and the next thing we saw was that a dinner plate had fallen on the rug. When a cup flew through the air and smashed against the fireplace the boys just ran. Cats scattered everywhere. Most darted out of the back door. But one tabby stayed and squinted, showing no consternation, as if he had seen it all before. The kittens hid under the settle, peering at me with their little green eyes all luminous and startled. I was really afraid, but I was so curious that I was rooted to the spot waiting for something else to happen.

Rachel came back into the room with a bag of sherbet pips, what we used to call tom thumbs, in her hand. She clucked with her tongue and bent to pick up the pieces of the broken cup. 'He been at it again then,' she said as much to herself as to me. 'Every darn summer without a miss.'

She turned to me and gave me the bag of sweets. 'There now. You take these an' make sure you do share 'em.' She gave me no explanation of anything, but showed me kindly to the back door.

I can never see sherbet sweets without thinking of that day!

The Haunting of Maggots Castle

Hallowe'en was always a favourite time for all the children in our village. There was, of course, no trick or treating, or pumpkins for that matter, as they became popular at a later date due to the American influence. Our Hallowe'en lanterns were made from turnip or swede. These were not at all easy to carve, so most children begged their father to hollow them out and cut out the eyes, nose and mouth for them.

We didn't have parties, as such, it was more like a gaggle of excited children, who all wished to walk around the village after dark looking for ghosts, and frightening themselves deliciously in the process. One or more adults would volunteer to accompany us, and get into the spirit of things. We would often dress up for the occasion. These were not shop bought costumes for none of us were really aware that they might exist and, if we did, none could have afforded them. So these costumes were always home-made from scraps of material that were once curtains or sheets. Some of us were really adventurous and splashed dye or paint on them to represent blood. We often used our mothers' or older sisters' make-up to paint our faces. We made tall witches' hats from the cardboard of cornflake boxes, and painted them black. Most people had a broom or besom in their garden, and this was handy for us children to use on Hallowe'en for witches' broomsticks.

The walk around the village in the dark was exciting, and made all the more so as certain spots were very dark indeed; street lighting was then minimal, and in any case lights went out everywhere at 10 pm. Sometimes, though, there was a full moon casting its eerie light, making shadows and silhouettes, turning the landscape into a strange world full of magic.

Due to the fact that my father loved Hallowe'en, and enjoyed having the children round for storytelling at the end of our walk, we nearly always ended up back at our house. There we would sit on the living room floor in front of an open fire by candlelight, sipping hot cocoa and anticipating the scary ghost stories that might get told. The fire would crackle and there would be this feeling of safety and warmth, and a little tingle of fear about the story that was to come.

My father was a good storyteller, as were so many people in those days before television. One of the best-loved stories of the village was 'The Haunting of Maggots Castle'. Some child was always bound to call out for it to be told on Hallowe'en. And a chorus of 'Yes! Yes! The Haunting of Maggots Castle!' would go up around the room.

So father would go through his little ritual of walking over to his drinks cupboard, taking a glass and pouring a small shot of whisky; he would then stand with his back to the fire and look at the eager little faces all awaiting for him to begin.

This is how the story went:

'Now, down between Ushent [Urchfont] an' Crook 'Ood ther be a place as you all know, called The Folly. An' down thur were a gurt big mansion that were known as Maggots Castle. All that is left on it now is a gurt big cellar, full o' water, as like as not.

Now, back in the ol' days Maggots Castle were owned by a very wicked man. So wicked, in fact, that they say the Devil 'iself should of come an' took 'un. Young girls from the village would go down thur lookin' for work, as servant maids and the like, and they was never seen again!

People would go down there enquirin' as to their whereabouts, but the squire o' Maggots Castle would see 'em off wi' his dogs. Gurt big bull mastiffs them dogs was, so people feared for their lives when these hounds was set at 'em. Some people started to whisper that these missin' girls had been ill treated, and then murdered by the squire. But no one could prove nuthin' at all. An' the wicked squire was rich an' powerful, and even the law couldn't touch him, as he had a lot of influence in these parts.

Then one day, a young an' sparky girl called Sarah, from the village, decided to go down to Maggots Castle to find what had happened to her sister.

'Er sister had gone down a year back, and no one had seen hide nor hair of 'er ever since. Sarah had told her parents she was going to do this. They were afraid, and begged her not to go. Sarah was a clever girl, and she knew that 'er parents were right to be afraid, but she had so dearly loved her sister Jane, and missed her so much, that she was determined to go and find out where she was. So it was that brave Sarah went an' walked to Maggots Castle. 'Er knees did tremble when she stood at them gurt big gates. No one was allowed to enter, unless invited.

When a servant comes up to them gates, Sarah pretends that it is a job she is after. Well, Sarah was a comely girl, and lively, so the servant lets her in, knowin' that his master would approve. Soon Sarah was shown into the squire's study. She was tremblin' badly, and stuttered when she spoke. The squire was used to this, and soon he offered her a job as a maidservant in the house.

It was the day before New Year's Eve that she was taken on as maid in the squire's house, and cold and frosty it were, the ground as hard as iron.

Sarah had to sleep in an attic room in the big house, and it were freezin' cold. Poor thing didn't have even a small fire in thur. She got into the little hard narrow bed wi' all 'er clothes still on so cold was it. She dozed fitfully, an' down below in a different, decadent, an' warm place, she could 'ear the squire carousing wi' his evil friends way into the night.

But worse still, whether she was asleep or awake she never did know, she could see the spirits of the poor dead maids that had been murdered all around her bed, weepin' an' wailin' and tryin' to tell 'er what had happened to them.

Then her own dear sister Jane too appeared, but Jane was warnin' her to leave as fast as she could. Sarah tossed and turned in her bed all night long, but she knew that she could not go runnin' away in the middle o' the night or the big dogs would be set on 'er. She were so glad when the pale dawn light crept through 'er window, the night being gone at last. Also glad that the squire had not visited her, as she feared that he might, and glad that the poor ghosts had all gone. She wanted to weep for Jane, but knew that she must keep her head, and keep quiet, if she was to get out of there alive. So she rose to start her work of layin' fires and cleaning grates.

At eleven o' the clock that mornin' the squire sent for her. She was told to go to his study.

Tremblin' from head to foot she knocked on the door and was told to enter. To her surprise, fearin' she was to be alone wi' him, she saw him sat drinking brandy, an' a lady was at his elbow, dressed all in finery. The lady looked at Sarah with undisguised distaste. She had hair like fine spun gold an' a lovely face, marred by a cruel mouth an' vixen's eyes.

The squire looked at Sarah, takin' into account 'er comeliness, but treatin' her like she was a piece of livestock to be bought at market. He too had dark cruel eyes, and his teeth were white and sharp. He told Sarah that the lady would be findin' a pretty dress for her to wear, as she was to meet him later that night after the New Year's Eve ball he was attendin' elsewhere.

She was to be bathed and then dressed in silk. The lady and the squire looked at one another an' laughed cruelly. Sarah stood stock still an' looked down at 'er feet. Her heart was really pounding now as she could guess what it all meant. She feared for her life. She knew that she would have to think of a plan right quick if she were to stay alive. So she decided on one straight away; she were a clever girl, and brave.

She went an' bathed an' had the silk dress fitted. It was a dress she had never seen the like of, but she took no pleasure in it. When that had all been done she went straight round to the kennels, where John the kennel man was busy chopping up a carcass for the dogs. She purposefully flirted wi' John, who was surprised that such a comely girl had taken such a shine to 'im.

Sarah was cunning an' she soon 'ad John eatin' out of 'er hand. Then she told him that she would give him a kiss if he let 'er out of the gates just before midnight, so that she might go an' visit her parents for half an hour on New Year's Eve. John, who couldn't believe his luck, promised to keep the dogs locked in their kennels, but told her she must be no longer than half an hour. He didn't like the sound of it really, as he was mightily afraid of his master. But he could not stop thinkin' of Sarah's sweet cherry lips, and half an hour was so little to ask.

So, sure enough, at 11.30 that night John let Sarah out of the big gates, and Sarah swore she would soon be back. Sarah's knees was tremblin' as she pulled her woollen cloak around her and set off into the night. There were no moon, thank God, an' the night were pitch black. She had to follow the old straight path, that is the chalk path, which shines up even on the darkest nights, to see where she was going. She could hear the big dogs barkin' in the kennels some way behind her now. And for a moment she feared that John would not keep his word, and she had visions of the lolling tongues and sharp white teeth that would tear at her if they caught her. But brave Sarah still went about her plan, her poor sister's ghost vivid in her mind. She scrambled up the steep banks that rose either side of the main track, slippin' and slidin' in her haste.

Then she found what she were lookin' for. It were a gurt boulder of pure white chalk and stone, fallen down from the banks and tree roots. She had such a job to push 'un. But her fear and determination gave her strength she did not know she had. And before long she had thik thur boulder placed right where she wanted 'un. That is right in the track where a carriage wheel might hit 'un!

Then she scrambled right back up the bank and hid herself. She waited for what seemed like an age, but of course was not. She could hear the church clock strikin' in the village. She counted twelve. Yes, it was midnight! She knew that it wouldn' be long now 'til the carriage appeared.

For that monster of a man had told her to be ready in her dress at midnight for his return. Soon she heard the horses' hooves and the clatter of the carriage. They were advancin' at speed as was the squire's wont. She could hear that he had friends inside too; they had been drinking and their raucous laughter rang out in the night. She saw the horses try to swerve as they saw the boulder. But the driver could not hold them at the speed that his master made him drive. One of the wheels of the carriage hit the boulder square on, and tilted the carriage dangerously. The horses, in great fear, reared an' shied, trying to flee in terror. But this tipped the carriage right over, and the horses in their traces got toppled too.

The screams coming from man and animal alike sickened Sarah, and stayed with her for the rest of her life. She did not dare to look at the carnage, but she heard groans, and then an ominous silence descended. Sarah did not wait, but ran as fast as she could home to the village. She went into their cottage and locked the door, not even speaking to her parents who woke and were so glad to see 'er. The next day, when she awoke, she realised that at last she was safe. Tale had come to the village that the squire of Maggots Castle and some of his cronies had died the night before, crushed in their carriage.

And to this day if you was to go down thik thur track that leads to Maggots Castle, on twelve midnight on a New Year's Eve, then you would see a ghostly carriage an' four. But beware! Many a man 'as died at the very sight of it!'

Poltergeists at Alton Barnes

Whilst I was living in the village of Bishops Cannings in the 1970s, I was told a strange tale of the poltergeist of Alton Barnes.

We were fortunate enough to still have fresh bread delivered to our doorstep at that time. A middle-aged lady who originally came from local farming stock brought it, driving a van that was a small mobile shop. She was rather solid, and red-faced from long days in the open air tending to the farm animals. She had, in fact, hand milked her father's herd of cows at one time, and then went on to use the milking machine as things progressed. She was a very straightforward sort of lady, and little inclined to small talk, so it came as a real surprise when one day she started to tell me what had happened to her at Alton Barnes, a couple of villages away.

It was a very hot summer's afternoon, around 4 pm, when she came to my door to deliver my bread. This was her usual time, but she looked rather hot and bothered that day. I thought it must be the heat, as she had to travel around in her van with the sun streaming in through the windscreen all day long. So I offered her a nice cool drink of lemon squash with ice in it.

After she had finished her drink, inquired about my dogs and told me an anecdote or two about Monty, her aged cat, for she loved animals of all kinds, she suddenly burst out, 'I really do not want to go to that house at Alton Barnes!'

I was taken aback as she always seemed such a calm and placid lady who would take most things in her stride. Thinking that maybe there was a vicious dog at this house, or perhaps a cantankerous customer, I asked her if that was so, hoping that maybe I could give some sort of advice. She was a nice kindly person so I just wished to help.

'Well unless you know what to do about poltergeists, I don't think there's anything you can do,' she replied.

I was speechless for a moment. I gazed out at my sunlit garden; it was one of those very hot days when everything is completely still. Not a bird flew, not even a breath of breeze moved. My dogs, usually so lively, were all lying on the cool tiled floor of the kitchen in the shade. It did not seem like very ghostly weather, no darkness, no mists, no howling winds, just bright clear sunshine.

'Poltergeists?' I asked timidly when I was able to find words again.

She put down the huge wicker breadbasket that she carried, and began her tale. 'Well it all started about two summers ago. I was asked by a couple that lived in a large Victorian house in Alton Barnes if I could deliver bread for them. They often had guests to stay and the order would sometimes be quite large. So naturally I agreed. They seemed like nice people, and it turned out there was a lucrative piece of custom to be had.

The only drawback was to be that they were often not in at the time when I had to deliver the bread to them. Well, I told them that I could not possibly leave the bread outside, as animals could get at it, or it could even be stolen. So they suggested I leave the bread on a shelf in the large porch at the front of their house. Well, I say porch, but it is more like one of those lovely old Victorian conservatories in miniature really.

They also said that they would leave the money for the bread on the shelf too, and they would give me a spare key for the porch.

Well, I agreed to this as it all seemed quite straightforward and, as I said, they were nice people. So I began to deliver the bread to them. My first delivery was on a cold winter's afternoon in November, so it was nearly dark by the time I had arrived at the house. They had left the outside light on for me, and everything was peaceful and quiet. I went inside the porch, put the bread on the shelf, collected my money, and left without any mishap.

And it remained quiet, until the summer came. I think it would have been late May or early June when the trouble really began. And every summer without fail it has continued.

Well, when it began for me it was a lovely summer's day, not unlike today. I was feeling happy, as that delivery in Alton Barnes was to be my last one before returning home. I was thinking to myself that I must remember to pick up a tin of pilchards from the van, to take indoors with me when I arrived home, to give to my dear old cat, Monty, as a treat.

I went up the path to the porch. All seemed quiet as usual; no one was at home, of course, as I expected. I put the key in the lock, turned it, and went in the porch as I usually did. I was just putting the bread on the shelf, when suddenly, as if from nowhere, a hail of stones rapped against the windows! I nearly jumped right out of my skin!

After the initial shock of this I recovered enough to wonder if it was children playing pranks. So I peeped through the window-panes on all sides and could see no sign of anything or anyone. The house stood on its own in large gardens; the only approach was from the front drive. Yet all was still, and no one was anywhere to be seen.

I felt really quite shaken; the noise of the stones against the glass had been very loud in this quiet place. It really did unnerve me. I decided to leave immediately as things just did not feel right there somehow. Yet it was a lovely day, and the house was beautiful, set in a wonderful rural spot as it was – it just didn't make sense.

Then, as I stood pondering on this, there was a loud sort of 'pop', and then a gardening boot hit me directly on the back of the head as if it had been thrown with force! Of course there was no one in the porch, or outside it, and the boot had obviously come from where there was some other footwear on the floor directly beneath me.

My nerve broke completely then. I ran for the door, but I was encumbered by my big breadbasket. Before I could reach the door to leave *something had pulled the inside doormat from under my feet.* This sent me flying backwards, I found myself thumping to the ground in rather an ungraceful way, right onto my backside!

I am afraid to admit that I burst into tears at the fright and the shock of it all. Then, as if to humiliate me the more, the money that had been left on the shelf for me to collect was thrown by some unseen hand in a shower over me. I got up and ran out to my van, leaping inside and locking the doors. I was shaking so much that I could not drive for a good ten minutes, even though I really wanted to get away from that place.

I have heard of poltergeists, and I believe that is what I encountered there at the house in Alton Barnes. I have never experienced this before, though I have seen ghosts a few times. This one keeps getting up to its antics every summer, and I have not got used to it at all. I am still afraid of it, but I hate the thought of letting down these nice people who own the house. I have not mentioned it to them, and they have never said anything about it to me on the rare occasions that I see them. So perhaps nothing like what happens to me has ever happened to them, or if it has, perhaps they are not talking about it.

I have to pluck up the courage to go to that house for the last time today, and thank God it is the last time too. These people are selling the house, you see, and moving, which is quite odd really considering that they were always saying how much they loved it there. I will not be taking on the custom of the new owners, I can tell you. I have been frightened enough by that *thing*.'

She dabbed her weather-beaten face with her handkerchief. There were beads of perspiration rolling down her cheeks, and I couldn't help but wonder if it were more due to fear than the heat. Her rough hands trembled as she lifted her basket. 'Well, I best go and get it over with,' she said, walking towards her van.

I found myself feeling worried for her as she left. I knew that she would come to no harm, but her fear was very real. And so ends the story of the poltergeist of Alton Barnes, except that it did not really end there as I had another, and different, story told to me about a poltergeist in Alton Barnes some years later.

The Old Man in the Brown Raincoat

This story was told to me in the early 1970s, by a young man who worked on a farm in Bishops Cannings. It was rather a gloomy day in February and I was grooming a pony. I worked on the same farm as the lad at that time, as a groom, so he would often come and chat for a while. The lad was not altogether imaginative by nature, so it came as quite a surprise when one day he stood next to me quite silent, then he tentatively said, 'Do you believe in ghosts?'

This quite astonished me, coming as it did from him, as he was one of the last people I would imagine that would ask me this question. But I replied that I knew that there were such things as ghosts. He seemed mightily relieved at this, indeed he seemed so cheered by my answer that I began to be afraid he might just walk off satisfied, without explaining what was behind his inquiry!

When I asked him to elaborate, he looked very uneasy and did not seem in a hurry to reply. Then, he cleared his throat, and in his slow, quiet voice told this tale:

'I'd just got this new Mini Cooper see, you'll have noticed her parked in the yard? And I was just dyin' to show her off to me mates, this was last November.

Well I asked the two Richards that work here and Pete the foreman if they'd like to go for a spin in her, and we could have a drink or two an' a game of pool, and just see what was around, you know, girl-wise.

First of all we goes into the pub here. They had a few bevies, but I didn't as I was drivin', but I didn't mind that as the last thing I would have wanted was a prang in me new car.

Anyway, it was a Saturday night, and in the pub we met up with some people who invited us to a private party at Etchilhampton. I was a bit reluctant, to tell the truth. I mean I had only just got me Mini then, and she can go some, and I knew the boys would want me to put my foot down and show off on the way there. And it would mean that I couldn't have a drink all night too, and not even any of the old waccy baccy either. But I gave in, me being the fool that I am, and said that we would see them later on. They told us we could join them any time as the party was to go on all night.

It was around eleven thirty that we all piled into the Mini, intent on going to this party. We were all in high spirits. The usual comments were being bandied around, you know, like had I noticed the girl with the long blonde hair and the long legs, the one in the mini skirt, and how they hoped she might be still at the party when we got there. I mean, in truth, all of us would have been too shy to speak to her anyway! Except perhaps for blond Richard who had necked five pints of strong ale.

So off we all set towards Coate, the next village, in the Mini. It was a very cold dark night, and it started to rain really hard as we left Bishops Cannings. It was raining so hard, in fact, that I had to have my windscreen wipers on fast; yet I was still finding it difficult to see the road in front of me clearly. I almost decided to call it a night and go home, but the boys insisted that they wanted to go to this party. So on we went in the pouring rain. I had to have my face really close to the windscreen to see through it properly.

Pete sat next to me in the front, and the two Richards sat in the back. They were rather drunk and they were singing bawdy songs and making us all laugh. The car was running beautifully, despite the rain, and I couldn't help but show her off a bit, so were going along at about 70 mph on the straight piece of road between Coate and Etchilhampton.

I started to brake and slow her down a bit as we came towards the T-junction that led off to Etchilhampton village. Then it happened.

It occurred in a split second I suppose, but I always kind of feel that it took place in slow motion, so to speak. A little old man in a brown raincoat that was tied round with binder twine stepped right out in front of me! Yes, *right in front of me*. And I was travelling then at about 45 mph as I approached the T-junction.

I saw his figure, as large as life, step right out in front of me in the headlights of the Mini. I jammed on the brakes and screeched to a halt, sending my passengers all ways. A load of swearing came from the back of the car, and Pete shouted, "What the hell is going on?"

I jumped out of the car in the pouring rain, my heart right up in my mouth. I expected to find the old man lying injured, or worse, on the side of the road, but I had heard no thump. You would expect to hear a sickening thud if you hit something. I remembered this as I had hit a dog by accident before on the road. The rain ran in rivers down my face and over my body, soaking me to the skin, as I stood there frantically looking around with a torch I kept in the car. I had only a shirt and jeans on and I was shivering from cold and shock.

Pete got out beside me, asking if I had thought I had hit an animal or something, as wild animals often showed up in the headlights along that lonely stretch of road. I couldn't even answer him, I was still frantically searching the roadside and banks, and I even ran down into the fields either side of the road. But there was no one and nothing to be seen anywhere.

Eventually I got back into the car; I just sat there unable to move or speak for a while, I was now wet, cold and really shocked. The boys, all quiet now, asked me what was wrong. I told them what I had seen. They all fell completely silent, looking at me half scared and half in disbelief. They told me they had seen nothing at all. Not even Pete, and he had been sitting alongside me in the front of the car.

Well, I'll tell you this, we didn't go to that party. I turned around and took them all home, and went home myself too, and boy was I glad to get back into some warmth and light after that! Nothing like this had ever happened to me before, and I hope to God it never does again.

I even returned to the spot the next morning to check it out by daylight. But there was nothing to be seen. No human footprints were there, other than my own, in the mud. I felt so bad about it I even listened to the local news in case there was a report of an accident there. If there had been I was going to go straight to the police and own up. But there was not a report of any accident there. I listened all day long to the radio news just in case.

I can still see him, that little old man in his brown raincoat; in my mind I mean. He seemed as real as you or me. But the only thing he could have been … was a ghost!'

The young man who told this story was not the last person to see the little old man at this road junction; several people who are unconnected have told the same tale. It is always the same, the little old man in a brown raincoat appears and crosses the road, it is always on that stretch of road, and it is always raining at the time.

The Black Creature at the Crossroads

The events I am about to relate happened to my partner and myself. It was a very cold February night in 1992 and a gibbous moon hung in the sky, a pale moon, icy and yellow. We had been out for the evening and were in good spirits as we travelled back towards Market Lavington, where we were living at that time. We were in our rather old and rattling van; the heater was very fickle in it, and I remember longing to get home to warm myself up.

It was around 12.30 am when we reached the poplar trees that lined the road towards the Black Dog Crossroads. Suddenly, Kevin, who was driving, had to use the brakes quickly as something was about to cross the road about 100 yards in front of us.

Clouds had gone over the moon, leaving the night very dark. But we could just make out in the headlights of the van, a huge, long, black form slowly crossing the road in the distance. We both stared transfixed. It was some sort of creature, but what it was we could not tell. It was monstrous in size, being about 15 feet from nose to tail, and it seemed to be pure black in colour.

It was certainly not feline, and, to my mind, not canine either. I have always been a great animal lover, and I know about all kinds of creatures, having studied them. Animals in one form or another have always been a part of my life, so I am amply qualified to distinguish between the different species. The gait that this creature had reminded me of something reptilian, it moved like a giant lizard or crocodile might. In fact it was the way that it was moving, along with its size, that made us shudder the most. Then, it must have turned its head our way because for one moment its eyes shone like two small lamps in the darkness, obviously catching the reflection from the headlights of the van.

It then lumbered off surprisingly quickly, and was soon gone through the fence and into the nearby fields. We got out of the van with some trepidation. Both of us are fairly courageous people, but the size of this thing was quite daunting. We carefully looked around; we had no torch with us, but we could see no sign of it anywhere. Either it had decided to lie low in the hedgerow somewhere, or it had moved off really quickly into the night. The clouds were scurrying over the moon, and one moment it was bright moonlight, the next total darkness; it was not easy to see into the distance at all.

We decided to return to the van as we both felt cold, and rather shocked at what we had seen. We had heard of stories of the black dog, hence the name 'Black Dog Crossroads', but we had always thought of it in much more canine terms.

When we were inside the van we agreed how eerie the whole place felt, and we both really just wanted to get home. Kevin shuddered and told me that if he believed in evil he would swear it was abroad this night. I tried to remain level headed, thinking that perhaps the shock of seeing this creature had made us rather fanciful. But, despite this, the feeling remained with me and seemed to follow us back to our house.

Even when we got indoors, locked the door, turned on all the lights and warmed ourselves with a cup of tea and a nip of brandy, the feeling would not dissolve. Neither of us felt like going to bed, even though it was now in the wee hours, so I made more tea and sat and watched as Kevin kept going to the window and peering out into the darkness. We both said afterwards that we had this strange impression that the creature might have followed us home. Or if not the creature itself, something evil that had accompanied it. We could not shake this feeling off, despite the fact that we are people who are not easily spooked, nor afraid of wild creatures of any kind. And so we sat, cupping our hands around our steaming tea, too afraid to go to bed, too afraid to turn out the lights.

Later we both agreed that we felt as if we were being stalked by some evil entity. As though the creature had been linked to some dark force, malevolent and truly ghastly. We were sure that the creature we had seen was no dog, and yet we had witnessed it so close to the Black Dog Crossroads where tales of sightings of the huge black canine had abounded for years. We wondered to ourselves if we had seen the creature of the stories, and yet we had never heard accounts of it taking any other form than that of a large dog.

We had heard rumours too that if anyone should set eyes on the black dog, then misfortune would follow for them. We shivered at the thought.

The night we saw it we didn't go to bed. And it was not until the pale dawn came that we finally let ourselves lie down to rest. With the light of day the foul evil feeling subsided, but we did not go back to the scene to look for footprints, as we would have done in other circumstances, always looking for logical explanations; we somehow did not wish to revisit so soon. I think it was a dread that we might stir something up again. So we decided to leave it well alone. I do not think that a real escaped reptile, however large, would have left us with such unholy feeling after seeing it. Indeed we would have feared that less.

No really bad thing happened to us afterwards, but to this day we do not pass that place without a shudder. And we make it our business never to be in the vicinity after midnight.

The Little Boy in Avebury Churchyard

This story was told to me by a resident of Avebury whilst I was living there in the 1990s.

This particular lady was of a practical nature, as many country folk are. But she had lived in Avebury for most of her life and she was aware of what she termed 'the strangeness of the place'. She had not, until this incident happened to her one day as she crossed the churchyard in Avebury, had any such experiences before. So it is not surprising that when this occurred she first looked for a reasonable explanation for what she saw. Then, not finding one, she had to accept that something supernatural had happened to her.

Here is her story:

'I was walking one morning from Avebury Trusloe to the shop, you know, the little grocery store near the henge shop. It was around 10 am and I had my little two year old boy in the pushchair with me. It was a nice morning, sunny, but a bit on the cold side. It was at the beginning of March and I remember there were some daffs out in the graveyard. I was about to post a couple of things at the post office, inside the shop. It was my sister's birthday on the 10th, and I was thinking of getting her a card to post as well. I was also trying to remember what the odds and ends were that I needed to pick up at the shop, so my mind was full of this.

Well, we went and did our shopping, and I started for home in the usual way, that is across the graveyard, as this leads to a footpath that takes you back to Avebury Trusloe without having to walk near the main road. I remember stopping and looking at some of the flowers that had been freshly placed on a few of the graves. The churchyard is always beautifully tended, and I like to look at the flowers and notes that get left there.

Suddenly I glanced up, I just felt there was someone watching me. I saw a little boy dressed in a short brown jacket, brown trousers that reached to his knees, and white stockings that met the cropped trouser legs. He had a sort of brown cap on his head too. He had a sweet little face, with rosy cheeks, framed by thick curly brown hair that peeped out from beneath the cap. He looked so alive and full of mischief, and he was hopping on and off one of the very old tombs that are made up of stone slabs, right by the front door of the church.

I immediately presumed that as he was all dressed up in Victorian clothes he must have been a member of some theatre or something, or maybe a school trip, and that he had got bored, as children will, and had gone to play in the churchyard for a while. There were always events going on at Avebury Manor at that time, with people dressing up in period costume, re-enactments of things, falconry and jousting. So it was not unusual to see people around in Victorian clothing, or any other period dress.

Anyway, I thought that this youngster had strayed from the Manor grounds, and, as he looked only about eight years old, I decided to tell him to go back in there in case anyone found him missing and was worried.

As I approached the little boy, my own toddler pointed to him and shouted out and smiled. My son loved other children and always lit up when he saw them, hoping that they might play with him, being an only child at that time. So I walked on towards this boy, who was still hopping on and off the tomb. He did not seem to be taking any notice of us as I drew near but I supposed that was because he was so engrossed in his game. Then, to my great surprise, he disappeared. Yes, he vanished into thin air before my very eyes!

I ran up to the tomb and looked all around; he couldn't have got anywhere to hide in the time. I just stood there completely flabbergasted. I could not believe that this had happened. But my toddler had seen him too, and I had seen something that looked so very real, yes, it looked like a very real little boy to me, and yet it could not have been!

I haven't told many people this story in case they think I am bonkers. But I suppose that what I saw that day was a ghost. I had never seen a ghost before, and I have not seen one since. I also checked to see if anything particular was going on in Avebury Manor that day, but it wasn't. Everything was very quiet there that day.

You know the funny thing is that soon after seeing that little boy, or the ghost of that little boy to be more correct, I fell pregnant. Which is quite strange as I had been told that I was infertile after my first baby, due to cysts that had appeared on my ovaries. This had been a great disappointment to me and my husband, as we always wanted more than one child. Now I have another little boy as well. I mean, I don't know if it was connected in some way, but I must admit I did link it in my own mind, I don't know why. He really was a fine little boy. I shall always remember seeing him.'

The Phantom Funeral Cortège

This was a tale told to me by the very same lady who had told me about the Alton Barnes poltergeist (Chapter 4). She seems to have had several supernatural experiences, and in the old days would have been thought of as 'having the Sight'.

As explained in her other story, she was extremely hardworking and conscientious. I cannot remember her ever missing a day's work; when she said she would be there delivering the bread, she always was. She didn't seem to suffer from many ailments, perhaps due to a strong constitution, no doubt fortified by her many hours in the open air when she was doing farm work.

She was a quiet and unassuming lady, her complexion reddened by the time spent being subject to the forces of nature. She travelled to many homes in Wiltshire, delivering bread, and talked to many people as she did so. Yet I cannot ever remember her gossiping, or saying any bad word about anyone, save those who were unkind to animals. She was gentle, and a great animal lover. She warmed to me because we shared this love of animals, and it made her open up to tell me things that she might not have told others – that is, about her supernatural experiences. 'Most people nowadays would not understand,' she would say, and then I knew she was about to embark on another tale.

One dark December day when she came to deliver the delicious crusty cottage loaves I had ordered, she told me this story:

'It was a day a bit like today that it happened. I was up at Shepherd's Shore, along Beckhampton, delivering to the cowman there. As you know, the Wansdyke runs along there, and it crosses the road just at the point where the cowman's house is, well the main road now interrupts it. The house the cowman lives in used to be an old inn. I always feel it to be a spooky house. But the cowman and his wife and family seem to be perfectly happy there, and have never said that anything was amiss. But I wouldn't like to live there myself.

Well, like I say, it was a foggy early December afternoon. You know, one of those days when the fog falls all of a sudden, and then can lift just as fast and there is brilliant sunshine. Anyway, I pulled up at Shepherd's Shore with the bread order for the cowman, and his wife came out to the van as usual to buy some other odds and ends that she wanted. She loves to have a chat as she doesn't get out much what with the hours her husband works, and the fact that it is a very lonely place where they live, with no other houses for a few miles.

The fog came down really thickly as we talked and I got to worrying about the visibility on the road. So I told her I had better make a move and got back into my van. I was half hoping that the fog might lift a bit before I pulled off, as it can be a fast and busy road and has had many fatalities. It is not an easy pull-out from that house anyway, so I sat a while and wrote down in my book the goods the cowman's wife had just chosen; she liked to pay fortnightly as this coincided with her husband's pay days.

Soon, as I had expected, this being a day of fog coming down fast, then dispersing, the fog lifted. The fields around me were instantly bathed in clear winter sunshine, and I could see for miles again.

Then I saw it. Coming along the Wansdyke right towards me. It was about 400 yards off when I first spotted it. I was taken aback to say the least! For there, approaching me, were ten soldiers of some kind, dressed in brown tunics and cloaks, and with helmets on their heads that shone in the sun. Six of these soldiers were walking alongside a cart, pulled by a little chunky pony, and on that cart was what looked like a dead body wrapped up in cloth. Then there were two soldiers walking in front of the cart, and two behind. And, out in front, astride another brown pony, was a man carrying some sort of flag or banner, which was blowing in the breeze.

I sat in my van in total amazement as they travelled towards me. They looked real, very, very real. I think one of the foot soldiers that was not a pallbearer carried a drum. Well, there was certainly the sound of a beating drum coming from somewhere. I could hear it clearly. Then, just as quickly as it had cleared, the fog swirled in again. It was so thick that I could see nothing any more. I felt torn between feeling relieved and annoyed. I could no longer see them, the funeral cortège.

I just sat there, shivers running down my spine, half wondering to myself if they would appear out of the fog and cross the road in front of me. But they did not. I peered into the vapour until my eyes hurt, but of course I could not see a thing around me at all.

Soon the fog lifted again, along with a burst of sunshine. But there was nothing to be seen any more, save the farmland with some straggling gulls searching for food on the ground, the cattle lowing from their winter barns, and the long, long dyke that stretched for miles. Well, you know how open the land is there. There is nowhere anyone or anything the size of that procession could hide, or go out of sight. But there was no sign of it at all; it had disappeared!

Well, you could have knocked me down with a feather! What a strange and sombre sight. And, I must admit, I did get a bit superstitious about it. I was afraid it might be a premonition of death. And I worried in case it was some sort of message for me, about my loved ones or myself. But it turned out that my worry was unfounded, though I did have an elderly friend die soon after, but I put that down to coincidence, as she had been ill for some time.

Of course I have been back there, delivering the bread as usual, many times since. But, you know, I have never seen it again, the funeral cortège.'

All Hallows Haunting

This is the story of the first ever sighting I had of a ghost. I was 12 years old and lived in the village of Urchfont at the time. It was Hallowe'en. A more clichéd time to see a ghost is unimaginable. But see one I did.

I had been doing the usual things most of us did back then on Hallowe'en. The carved out swedes and turnips were glowing, showing ghastly faces, with the candle stubs burning inside. We had done our village walkabout, a group of children exploring with bravado, an adult leading. Stories had been told on our return, great fun and laughter had been had, and the thrill of a scary story still lingered. The big coal fire had died in the hearth, and my parents were telling me it was bedtime, and that I was to hurry and finish my cocoa.

For once I did not argue about going up to bed, or plead for just one more story, or another cup of steaming chocolate. I smiled inwardly to myself as I went up the stairs to my room, my little terrier trotting along behind me, waiting, as was his wont, to snuggle up with me under the bedcovers. I smiled because I had a plan; a very exciting plan, to a twelve year old girl anyway. Earlier that evening, I had arranged with my friend Jane to sneak out of our houses and meet each other at midnight. Then we would at last be privy to what went on at the 'witching hour'. We were both intrigued as we had heard tales of witches flying on broomsticks and the dead walking.

We knew that neither her parents nor mine would have agreed to let us do this. So, curiosity got the better of fear and we agreed to meet halfway between her house and mine. That meant meeting at what was commonly known as 'The Blackboards', a wooden boarded fence, once painted black, which edged the perimeter of the grounds of Urchfont Manor. This was a walk for both of us from where we each lived.

I remember feeling excited, and afraid, at the prospect of being out at the 'witching hour'. I looked from my bedroom window; it was already dark, very dark, the street lamps had long gone out and most decent folk were in bed.

I got under the covers with my tee shirt and jeans still on. Charlie, my little dog, snuggled into me and was soon snoring, as dogs often seem to be able to do. I left my lamp on and read a book. It was still only 11 pm; time seemed to pass so slowly. I couldn't concentrate on my book and kept looking at the hands on the clock that sat by my bedside lamp. Soon my father called out to me to turn off the lamp and go to sleep. I dutifully turned off the lamp without any of the usual protestations.

In the darkness time seemed to pass at an even slower pace. All that I could do was lie there listening to Charlie's snores and the gentle ticking of the clock. I thought I would go mad with impatience, and the anticipation of it all.

After a while I heard my brother come home from the pub and go up to his room. No bother there, I thought, a few pints of beer always sent him straight into a deep sleep. At eleven thirty I could hear my dad snoring. The household had at last gone to sleep. Now I was beside myself with excitement, what an adventure I was about to have! I had never sneaked out like this before.

I couldn't help but wonder what Jane and I might see. I trembled at the thought of zombies, or even the Devil himself. Our neighbour, Mrs Whitbread, had told us that the Devil was always abroad on Hallowe'en. In fact, she told us once that his hoof mark had been seen, left imprinted in the mud and still smoking when morning arrived!

Fifteen minutes to twelve, and I was out of bed and trying to coax a grumpy terrier to come with me without making a noise. I decided not to pull on my jumper until I got out of the house, as the action always made my little dog bark in anticipation of a walk.

I carried Charlie downstairs underneath my arm, the jumper in my other hand. It was very dark in the kitchen as no light was ever left on at night in the house. I had planned well, though, and quickly found my torch and outdoor clothing. Then I realised that I would have to go back upstairs, as I had forgotten to do the old trick of putting the pillows under the bedcovers, to make it look as thought there was someone in the bed sleeping. I giggled to myself quietly as I did this, nearly making Charlie bark with excitement in the process. I went back downstairs as stealthily as I could, and pulled on my coat and boots whilst holding Charlie's jaws firmly shut at the same time to stop him making a noise. I knew that once we were outside he would forget the barking, and that he would just be eager to get going on a walk.

Silently we left the house, and as I quietly shut the back door and walked down the path and out onto the pavement I felt a surge of excitement and exhilaration. I had done it! No one had woken up. No lights had come on in the house. No one knew we were out.

It was a crisp, clear night. I could see some of the constellations shining brightly overhead. There was no moon. Charlie and I walked from our house towards The Blackboards. He was sniffing everywhere at the fresh scents, which were made more pungent by the cold air, and stopping now and then to cock his leg. It was very dark, and I had begun to realise what it really felt like for a twelve year old girl to be out alone late at night. I suddenly felt immensely glad that I had Charlie with me. Not one of the houses we passed had a light on. People in those days rarely stayed up late, especially on a weekday.

I became aware of every sound, as everything appeared to be so very silent all around me. I could hear a cow coughing in a field half a mile away and a late train down on the railway track that ran through the Folly; the cold night air was carrying the sounds and amplifying them.

We soon reached The Blackboards. I half expected to see Jane waiting there already, but she had not yet arrived. I wished she had been there. I didn't exactly feel afraid, but I was a little uncomfortable. It wasn't the dark, because I liked it, or even the supernatural, but the distrust of strangers. The Moors Murders were still fresh in everyone's minds, and children had been warned not to talk to strangers.

Soon I heard the church clock striking, with its rather tinny sounding bell. I stood and shivered, and peered up the road leading in the direction of where Jane would be coming from. Still there was no sign of her. Perhaps she had not managed to escape as I had. I was feeling very uneasy by now, and I nearly decided to turn around and just go back home. But I was torn with the thought that Jane might turn up late and wait around all alone for ages. She, after all, would not even have a dog with her. So I decided to stay put.

A little after midnight Charlie's hackles went up and he started to growl. His eyes were fixed on a spot on The Blackboards fence. He must have sensed something, as he could not see either over or through the fence. I was feeling very jittery by now; I kept on looking around me, but I could see nothing and no one. I was getting really cold too, and I was rubbing my hands together to try and drive out the chill.

Then Charlie growled again, a low deep growl that he always used when he feared something, or was unsure. Again, he was looking towards the fence. I plucked up the courage to walk closer to it, trying to pull Charlie with me, but he dug his heels in and would not go. I was astounded, as Charlie was a brave little soul who would have usually faced out anything.

Then I peeped over the fence. What I saw forced me to put my hand quickly to my mouth to stifle a scream. About 100 yards in front of me stood a man, and he was looking directly at me! I just froze to the spot. My heart was pounding, my mouth had gone dry and my knees were weak from fear. I was totally alone, a strange man was just over the fence and worst of all he had seen me.

I just stood there staring at this man; I didn't know what to do, I felt too weak to run. Charlie, picking up on my terror, started to bark and tried to pull me homewards. It was then that I noticed something very strange. At first I had just been aware that this man was quite tall, and that he was wearing what appeared to be a long raincoat and a trilby hat. I wasn't able to see his features clearly. The basement lights were still on in the manor house, *and I could actually see these lights shining right through this man as though he were transparent*. It was then I realised that this was not a living man at all. He was what some people would call a ghost!

I stared in fascination for a few minutes; the figure did not move at all, but it remained facing me, which was quite unnerving. Then Charlie started to bark, but this time he was looking down the road. I glanced down the road too, just for a split second, wondering if it was Jane at last. When I turned to look at the figure again it was gone.

The next thing that I knew was that Jane was running towards me, excited and laughing. She said that her parents had been late going to bed, and that she had waited for what seemed an age to creep out. And then, as she was about to leave, she had knocked something over in the dark. It had made a loud bang, but she had run out of the house anyway. I could hardly take in what she was saying as I was still trying to recover from my experience with the ghost. And what followed gave me no chance to discuss it with her.

Jane's father, who had heard the commotion in the house, had followed her and was soon upon us. He was very angry and gave us both a dressing down, and a stern reminder of what can happen to a couple of young girls alone late at night in the dark. Then he and Jane walked me safely home, and he assured me that he would be seeing my parents about it all the next day.

I slept very little that night, what with the experience that I had had and the anticipation of what my parents would say when Jane's father told them what we had been doing. So, when morning arrived, and I was sitting in front of the old range drinking a comforting cup of hot tea, I decided to tell my parents what had happened.

When I had told my story my mother asked me to describe the ghostly figure as best as I could to her. After I had finished, she turned to my father and said, 'Well there, Les! That sounds just like she seen Mr Pollack!' My father looked at her, then at me, and then slowly shook his head as if to play it all down. He went on to reprimand me for creeping out of the house at night. Nothing else was said about the matter; perhaps, looking back, it was because they thought I might get worried about what I had seen.

But I knew who Mr Pollack was. He was the last real squire, or Lord of the Manor, as people called it. And due to some terrible financial disaster, brought about by the war, he had lost all hope. He went to the kennels first and shot his gun dogs, then he went back into the manor and shot his wife and children dead, then he put the revolver into the roof of his mouth and pulled the trigger. Everyone in the village at that time knew this tragic story. My mother and father had seen him often in their lifetime there. So I came to the conclusion that my mother was right, I had indeed seen his ghost!

The Rider on the Fine Bay Horse

The ancient and magnificent earthworks of Old Sarum stand out against the horizon as you enter Salisbury on the A345. This is a place of great wonder and beauty; once a castle built by the Plantagenets had stood there, and also a great cathedral that equalled in splendour the one now in Salisbury itself.

The ruins of the castle are still there, along with the foundations of the cathedral. The banks to the top where these are situated are very steep and huge, stately trees grow all around as you reach the plateau. Vast lawn-like expanses of ground sweep out before you at the summit and the views of the surrounding countryside are breathtaking.

The place somehow always has a magical feel about it, no matter what the time of day or year and whatever the weather. It attracts thousands of visitors from all over the world. Sometimes there are even battle re-enactments there to add to the atmosphere.

The following story was told to me by a young woman who regularly walked her dogs here. She had lived in the Salisbury area all her life, and so knew Old Sarum very well:

'It was a fine, sunny day in the first week of May, and it was nearly as hot as it might be in June. I thought myself very fortunate to have booked a holiday from work in such good weather. I love walking and I decided to spend my holiday on foot in some of my favourite local places. My boyfriend had been unable to arrange a holiday that coincided with mine, but I decided to make the best of it. My plan was to take a packed lunch every day, load the dogs into the car and drive to spots where I could go walking to my heart's content.

Old Sarum really isn't that far from where I live, but I love it there, and the dogs always have so much fun scrambling up and down the banks looking for rabbits, which, I might add, they never catch. It is a great place to wear out their seemingly boundless energy.

Well, on this particular day, they had run themselves ragged. So I decided to sit underneath one of the trees that overlook the ruins of the castle. I hoped that this might encourage the dogs to come and lie by me in the shade of the tree as it was so hot. Sure enough, soon they came over and took some water from me, and then lay next to me with their mouths open in that kind of satisfied smile that dogs have when they are happy yet tired. I was glad to sit too after the climb in the midday heat.

There were a few other walkers, but not that many as it was a weekday when most people were still at work. It was very relaxing sitting underneath this huge beech, I felt pleasantly warm and the ambience of the place was making me quite dreamy. I remember thinking that it would soon be time to eat my sandwiches, and how pleasantly different this lunch would be from the usual snatched break we always had in the cramped little office where I work. It was really so luxurious just to sit there with the sun filtering through the branches of the tree and the dogs stretched out each side of me. They did not seem to be in any more of a hurry to move off than I did.

Then, as I looked towards the castle ruins, I glimpsed a little procession of people and horses. What really caught my eye was the colour of their clothes. Then I realised that they were, in fact, all dressed in what looked like mediaeval attire.

I jumped up quickly to get a better view. This set the dogs barking furiously, so I put them on their leads to make sure that they could not chase the horses. I looked again, and saw that at the front of the cavalcade there was a young woman dressed in the most exquisite green. She was riding a fine bay horse, which was being led by what looked like a page or groom of some kind. He was very young, and had brown hair and a grey tunic. The rider was a rather handsome young woman, with long fair hair braided with ribbons, about 20 years of age, I thought.

The rest of the people followed along behind her, over the ramparts of the castle. They were not dressed in such sumptuous garments as she, and they were on foot, some of them leading small cobby ponies with packs on their backs. The only exception to this was a man at the very back who sat astride a big black horse. He had some kind of armour on that shone in the sun, and he carried a sword. I immediately felt that he was there to protect the lady on her journey, in case any harm should befall her.

I watched in absolute fascination. At first I thought they might be some players who had come to perform some sort of pageant. Well, they looked wonderfully authentic, so I decided to follow them and see the show. They carried on towards the old castle ruins, and I followed them at a distance;

they took no heed of me whatsoever, in fact they seemed completely oblivious to any onlookers.

Then, to my great surprise, they just vanished. I could not believe it! I ran towards where I had seen them, setting the dogs off barking again. I got to a vantage point on the banks and scanned the area. I looked around everywhere but they were nowhere to be seen. It was impossible that they should disappear from sight, there was nowhere for them to be hidden. After all there had been all those people, ponies and two horses!

I have told a few people about this experience, and several have said that I am not the first to relate such a thing. In fact, this very same procession has been witnessed before by others. But I have never seen it again, despite going there so regularly.

I have always really hoped to see the people – or should I say ghosts – again; they looked so real, and so enigmatic. I would like to know who they were and what they were doing. I was not scared at all by what happened. It was rather exciting, like stepping into a sort of time warp or something.'

Inside the Long Barrow

The following events were related to me by a lady who had come to Wiltshire to visit the West Kennet Long Barrow with her husband in 1992. They were both interested in archaeology and local history, so naturally they were drawn to see the magnificent Long Barrow, which sits to the west of Avebury in the downlands of 'the chalk'.

This is her story:

'My husband and I had decided to take some time off work and have a long weekend away. We went to stay with a friend of ours who lives in Marlborough. We adore the Wiltshire countryside and never tire of seeing the ancient sites like Avebury and Stonehenge.

On the Saturday afternoon of that weekend we decided that we would visit Avebury again, and also, on the way back to our friend's house, I wanted to make the last call of the day to the West Kennet Long Barrow. I remembered having seen it as a child and I had found it quite awesome then; I think I also might have been a little afraid. I remember it as being very dark inside, it is, after all, a tomb.

That Saturday was a really lovely day in mid October. The sunlight was that golden colour that comes with autumn, and the leaves on the trees were changing colour all around the henge at Avebury. It was so magnificent that we stayed a little overlong just enjoying the stone circle, and then we had a meal at the local pub.

So, by the time we were leaving Avebury the sun was already setting and we hurried along to West Kennet in our little car. We parked in the lay-by opposite Silbury Hill, which looked magnificent in the fading light. We stopped to ponder on the usual question – why it was there at all – and could not come up with any real answer, just like most people before us. Then we set out briskly on the little pathway that leads up to the Long Barrow.

There was no one else around; most people who were visiting had no doubt left before darkness set in, save for one couple whom we passed on the pathway as they were returning to their car. I remember feeling rather glad about us being the only ones there, as I am sure that to really enjoy the atmosphere of a place like the Long Barrow it is better to be alone.

I could not help feeling a shiver run up my spine as we approached the Long Barrow, for it seems to sit like some great crouching dragon on the landscape. It was silhouetted on the horizon as the sun was setting, with a few of the first stars appearing in a cold blue sky. My husband was in front and had reached the entrance already, scrambling excitedly around the huge megaliths that stand at the entrance of the tomb. He then disappeared inside, and soon popped out again grinning like a Cheshire Cat, saying how incredible it was.

I stayed outside the tomb for all of this time. I was almost overwhelmed by the magic of the place, and the amazing view of the surrounding downland. My husband was striding along the long top of the barrow. I knew that his mind would be full of things to do with the size, age and structure of the place, also questions about those who had built it. I always leave him to his own devices when he does this, as he likes time to ponder; and I knew that later on, over dinner, he would be telling us all his thoughts on the matter.

So I left him to it, as I was sure he would be a little while yet, and I scrambled down into the mouth of the tomb. I stood for some time at the entrance, peeping cautiously into what looked like a gaping hole of blackness. With the setting sun, the light was fading fast now outside and I knew that the inside of the chamber would be very dark. So I stood rather reluctantly looking in, seeing nothing save for the vague outline of the stones that line the inside of the tomb. We had not brought a torch with us as my husband always said that torchlight ruins the natural night sight that we are blessed with. So I had no option but to go into the chamber in the pitch dark.

At last, with some trepidation, I plucked up the courage to enter the tomb. The first thing I noticed was how warm it was inside. There had been a brisk wind whilst I was walking on the top of the barrow, but the interior was not at all cold. It smelled wonderfully earthy, and there was a sweet edge to that smell. I began to think about why some said that the long barrows were built in the shape of the womb. And indeed, there was a narrow opening that you pass through to enter, like the vagina, then it widens out into a much bigger pocket that resembles the actual womb itself. Death and birth – natural cycles – maybe the two are inseparable? I was so busy thinking about these things, and the fact that the tomb inside was so amazing, that I quite forgot my fear.

When I reached the womb-like cavity I found myself astounded, and touched. Other people had apparently recently visited and had left incense, candles, flowers and apples, like some kind of offering to forgotten gods. It was quite astonishing to me that there were still people in this modern-day world who would do such a thing. But there they were before my very eyes, these natural offerings to ancient deities, obviously proffered with much care and love.

I think it was then that I began to feel a little dizzy, or "heady" as I call it. I wondered at first if it was a bit of claustrophobia, the chamber being quite compact. But I soon dismissed this, as I have never suffered from such a thing before. Still, I decided that maybe it would be best to get out of the tomb and go and take some fresh air.

Just as I had left the candle-lit womb-like chamber and headed down the dark passage toward the entrance of the tomb, I suddenly found that I had become stationary. My mouth had gone quite dry, and my heart was pounding so loudly that I could hear it. I did not know the reason for this, until I realised my senses had worked before my brain had caught up with them.

I could hear what could only be described as a sort of sighing, breathing sound, which seemed to fill up the whole chamber with its presence. I was rooted to the spot with fear and the uncertainty of not knowing what might happen next. I tried to call for my husband, but only a croak came out of my throat. Then, in the darkness, it was as if many pairs of hands caressed me, on the face, the shoulders and back. I wanted to scream, but nothing came out. Sweat stood out on my cheeks. The loud breathing sound increased; I thought that I might actually faint. Then, at last, I was able to run out of the tomb. I just stood weakly outside the entrance, trembling. I had never experienced anything like this before, nor have I since. My husband found me there in quite a state of shock. He ran down inside the tomb himself, but nothing at all strange happened.

We hardly spoke on the way back to our friend's house. My husband is a man who finds it very hard to believe in anything supernatural; he thinks that there is a logical explanation for everything. As I did too, until that day.

Angelica is a friend of long standing to us both, so when we arrived at her house I told her what had happened in the tomb. She was astonished by my story. But she said that she would telephone a friend of hers, a lady called Frankie, who was a spiritualist and who might understand more of what had occurred.

I followed Angelica up to her bedroom and sat on her bed whilst she phoned Frankie. It all seemed surreal somehow. I had not even realised that Angelica had friends who were into that sort of thing as she had never mentioned anything like that to us before. Soon I found myself speaking to

Frankie, a softly spoken, seemingly gentle lady. I told her all that had happened in the tomb.

After I had finished she said, "Don't worry, it is just the ancestors trying to speak with you." Of course I asked why on earth would they choose me, after all, they were not *my* ancestors! But Frankie went on to say that perhaps if I had not reacted in such a fearful way they would have told me something; or perhaps they were trying to point a way that I needed to go on the journey of life. But, she added, it did not matter. The fact was that they had touched me, contacted me. And I had heard and felt them.

I did not quite know what to reply to all of this. I knew for certain that it would be pointless to relate to my husband what Frankie had said; he had no time for spiritualists. So I just thanked Frankie and Angelica, but decided in my mind to forget the whole business.

But I have not been able to forget it, as you can tell. It was all very real, I can assure you, and extremely strange. But still, to this day, I do not know why it happened to me.'

12

Young Billy at the Catherine Wheel

This story was told by an aunt of mine. She heard it from a good friend of long standing who lived in Tilshead in the early 1960s.

Families in those days would often ride out in their car on a Sunday afternoon, after a nice roast lunch, cooked at home, and do what was known as a 'Sunday afternoon jaunt'. That is, slowly driving around the narrow country roads sightseeing. This leisurely ride provided them with information on any changes happening locally, or they would just take pleasure in the lovely countryside as they passed by. These outings often ended with the whole family calling in at a favourite pub for a nice pint of ale or a cider, with lemonade and a packet of potato crisps for the children; this was, of course, a real treat that everyone looked forward to.

Well, on this particular afternoon, my aunt's friend Lizzie, her husband and their four children chose to visit the pub in Shrewton formerly called the Catherine Wheel, a favourite of theirs.

This is Lizzie's story:

'It was a hot day in July. We had all been out driving around in the car, after we had eaten a huge roast lunch. All the windows were down in the car as it was such scorching weather; there was not a cloud in the sky.

We had been up on one of the range roads that cross Salisbury Plain. We had stopped and got out for a little walk, but it was so hot that even we did not feel like walking too far that day. I mean, usually we go for miles; there is nothing like a good long walk to get the energy out of the kids. Anyway, this time it was just too hot, we were even too fatigued by it to enjoy the lovely wild flowers that grow on the Plain, or even the lucky sighting of some deer that we startled by a small copse. So we decided to go back to the car, and we all agreed that it was such thirsty weather that a drink in the Catherine Wheel would go down really well.

I suppose by the time we reached the pub it was late afternoon. The sun was still relentless, but we all decided that we would sit outside with our drinks and enjoy it – after all, summers in Britain can be very short. There were only a few people in the bar inside the pub. Out in the beer garden there was no one but us, and a lonely looking soldier sitting at one of the wooden tables, with a glass of beer in front of him, hardly touched. This was not, of course, unusual as the Catherine Wheel was often frequented by soldiers from the nearby camp.

I do not think I would have really noticed this soldier if it had not been that he looked so despondent sitting there, staring into his beer. I mentioned it to Bobby, my husband, and he just smiled and said something like, "I 'spect it's woman trouble." The kids didn't really take much notice of this soldier at all – you know what kids are, running about and playing, in a world of their own.

Well, we finished our first lot of drinks, and Bobby took the tray back into the pub to get refills for us all. Three of the kids were hopping on and off the wall by the road. Jennifer, our youngest, was playing with a small rubber ball, all by herself, as usual. Then Jenny came up to me and asked why the soldier looked so sad. She was always a perceptive little thing – she was the one in the family that always seemed to care about everyone and everything. I replied that I had no idea why the soldier looked as he did.

I remember glancing across at him. He had not even changed position from when we had arrived, and we had been there a good half an hour. He just sat there, staring at the same spot. He looked very young, probably about eighteen, at a guess. He had sandy coloured hair and thick sandy eyelashes to match. He was fresh faced, and would have been quite handsome if only he had smiled. My heart went out to him, he really did look so sad, and he reminded me of my own brother at that age.

To my surprise, Jenny suddenly skipped across to him. Holding her little head on one side, like some cheeky little robin, she asked him, "Why are you so sad?" He did not even look up at her. She waited a moment, then feeling rejected, and looking quite deflated, she gave up and went back to playing with her ball. I felt for her, but he was obviously so engrossed in some inner sorrow that he did not seem to notice her at all. I did feel it was odd that he didn't even look up, but I supposed it was just his preoccupation with whatever it was that was worrying him.

Bobby came back with the drinks and saw me looking at the young soldier. He admonished me, in a jovial way, to keep my nose out and leave the lad to it. "The trouble with you, Lizzie," he said, "is that you are like an old mother bantam hen, always fussin' and worryin'. Our Jen's just the same, she got it from her mother!" I laughed at this, but I still couldn't help but peep over to the young soldier every now and then. He looked in such a bad way, I was contemplating encouraging Bobby to go over and have a chat with him to try and cheer him up.

It was as I had been talking to Bobby that a very strange thing happened. The young soldier had disappeared! The only way out would have been to pass us; otherwise he would have needed to go through the pub and out of the front door. Curiosity got the better of me and I had to see where he could have gone, it had happened so fast! I ran inside the pub and looked around, then I went out of the front door of the pub and looked up and down the road; he was nowhere in sight.

I ran back and told Bobby. I asked the children if they had seen the young man leave. They all said no. That is, except Jenny. She said he had just "vanished". Down to earth Bobby went back into the pub himself. I followed hot on his heels. The landlord looked up enquiringly, "You looking fer someone?" he asked. I told him about the young soldier. I said that I was only enquiring as the young man had looked so forlorn that somehow I feared for him.

"Oh, Missus, no need to worry," replied the landlord. "You will have seen Billy."

"Billy?" I asked, rather bewildered.

"Yep. Billy. He's a ghost, Missus."

Bobby and I stared for a moment at one another, neither of us quite sure that we had just heard correctly what the landlord had said.

'All the worryin' in the world can't help Billy now, Missus. It is just his shade you have seen. He used to come in a lot when he were alive, about three years back. Nice enough young feller he were. But not the right sort for the army I am afraid. He was one o' them sensitive types. He hated it, being a soldier. He had made a big mistake see, joining up. I think he'd run away from home, and then joined up. A Brummy he was. Of course, once you are in the army it is very hard to get out. The shame of it is, Billy did find a way out. He killed himself, he did. Blew his own brains out up on the Plains with a revolver. A few people have seen his shade out there, you know, in the beer garden. You ain't the first to have seen 'im, and prob'ly won't be last. I even thought that I caught him out of the corner of me eye, sat out there, once meself." The landlord then seemed to have dismissed us, because he walked away and began to continue with polishing his beer glasses.

Me and Bobby were left to look at each other with disbelief at what he had told us. But the fact is that me, Bobby and all of the children had seen this ghost. It sends shivers down my spine to think of it.

We still do sometimes go to the Catherine Wheel, despite our experience. But do you know what? We never did see Billy again. I hope to God that means the poor soul has gone to his rest at last.'

13

The Grey Lady

This tale was told to me by a lady called Marilyn. She had lived in Trowbridge all her life; apart from the mid 1960s, that is, when she moved to the small village of Marden, near Devizes.

This is her story:

'My husband and I were newly married, and hoping to save some money to buy a house of our own. So, until we could achieve our dream, we decided to rent a modest little place. Anyway, we went for the cheapest little rented place that we could find, and that happened to be in Marden.

I must admit that I was quite amazed when I first saw the pretty thatched cottage that was up for rent at such a reasonable price. It was quite small, I grant you, but there was only the two of us, so we really did not need a lot of room; besides we were both out at work all day anyway. It had a really pretty cottage garden, again small, and a little wicket fence all around the front of the house. A narrow gravelled garden path wound its way to the front door. I suppose nowadays it would be called charming. My hubby reckoned it must have been built in the late 1700s.

It was mid April when we moved in, and a cherry tree stood in the garden pink with blossom. I remember thinking how dark it seemed inside the little house – it had such tiny windows that not much light seemed to be able to filter through. I was, of course, used to living in a very modern house amid the hustle and bustle of town life. I must admit that I viewed living in the countryside with some trepidation. My hubby, on the other hand, was a born and bred country person, used to village life and its serenity. I suddenly felt rather glad that I owned a car and could drive.

Looking back, I think it was the very first week we moved in that I became more and more disconcerted about being in the house. The winding narrow stairs creaked whenever you walked up or down them. And there always seemed to be some sort of strange tapping and clicking sounds, which my hubby kept reassuring me about, saying that it was just the old woodwork expanding after we had lit our first fire, then contracting again as the heat left. I am not at all sure that this convinced me, even then.

Then there was the mice. I hate mice with a vengeance. I mean, they scare me. They make me shudder just to see them, they always have. When I went into the kitchen of the cottage one evening I saw five of the little perishers, sitting on my breadboard, as bold as you like, nibbling up crumbs and then washing their whiskers with their dreadful little paws. I had just about had enough; I screamed the house down!

We had my hubby's twelve year old sister staying with us the night that the mice episode happened. She, being a country girl, laughed and said, "Cheeky little things!" But my nerves were becoming frayed and I made my hubby promise to put down traps. But then I had the horror of looking at their awful little grey, broken bodies in the traps, so I had to give that up too.

Also there was this cat that turned up every now and then. It was a horrible scraggy thing with only one eye, its grey fur quite matted, and it had a disgusting smell. I am not a cat lover by nature. I hate the way they will jump on your lap and stick their sharp talons into your legs, and then look at you as though they are quite entitled to do so. This cat would sometimes walk in through the back door, or jump in through the kitchen window, as though it owned the place. And no matter how many times I shooed it away, back it would come. I even got so angry I threw a shoe at it and hit it. All it did was sit and glare at me from afar with that one malevolent lamp of an eye, as if to say, "*That* will not deter me." My husband infuriated me by suggesting I should be glad of a cat turning up, as it would see to the mice.

I really disliked it the most when I had to stay in the cottage alone. It was always gloomy inside, even on the sunniest of days. And, once or twice, I could have sworn that I had heard footsteps overhead whilst I was sitting in the sitting room. This was rather worrying, as overhead was our bedroom. But I was totally alone in the house, and I knew that I was. I would creep up the stairs, poker in hand, to take a look in case someone had broken in. But the bedroom, needless to say, was always just as I had left it.

When I told my hubby this he put it down to the fact that I was a "townie", and that I had a fanciful imagination to boot. But it was not that at all. I began to really dislike the cottage. And, the funny thing is, I also began to feel that the cottage, or someone or thing in it, disliked me. I then told my hubby that I wanted to move, that being in the cottage was affecting my nerves. He could see how upset I was getting, so he did not argue, although he seemed to be happy with the little house; I think that maybe he had even become fond of the place. Anyway, after some persuading, he eventually agreed that we would move, but he did suggest trying it a little longer first, as we had been living there such a short space of time. I agreed to this, with the proviso that we would, in the interim, be looking for somewhere else. I just *knew* that I did not want to stay there. I was becoming anxious of being there alone, and I was not sleeping well.

Then one night I awoke, needing to use the toilet. There was only one lavatory in the house, and that was downstairs. I had often dreaded this happening, as I knew that I would have to negotiate the winding stairs in the middle of the night. It was bad enough having to do this in the daytime, as there was no window at the top of the stairs, and, despite the landing light, the staircase always remained full of shadows, making the goose pimples rise on my skin.

I was so afraid I nearly woke my hubby to come down the stairs with me. But I felt this would show me up as being rather childish. And anyway he did have a very physical and demanding job as a bricklayer, so he really did need his sleep. So, with my heart pounding, I descended the stairs, which seemed to creak even louder in the early hours.

I saw her before I even reached the bottom of the stairs. She was stood two stairs up. A tall figure dressed in a pale grey dress. The dress had a sheen on it, and it looked to be of the fashion of Victorian times. Her grey hair was scraped back into a tidy, if rather severe, bun. Her face was pale and sombre, and she seemed to be looking straight at me with wide, pale blue eyes. For some reason unbeknown to me, she looked very displeased. My heart was thumping madly by now, and I felt that I just might faint. I wanted to scream, or at least call to my hubby. But nothing came out of my mouth, not a sound.

I do not really know how long I stood there like that, the ghost and I face to face. It was probably, in reality, just a minute or two. But it seemed a very long time; then she just disappeared before my very eyes. I still remained stationary, even after she had gone. My knees were like jelly. It was not just the sight of her, it was some malevolence she projected at me. I had such a strong feeling that she definitely did not want me in the cottage.

Well, I can tell you, that was quite enough for me. I told my hubby what had happened and insisted that we really could not stay. He could see that my nerves were at breaking point, and so very soon we were packing our belongings ready to leave. He had managed to find us a nice little town house back in Trowbridge on a modern estate.

But, you know, the day we were leaving I went back into the house alone, just to check that we had left nothing behind. Hubby was waiting outside in the car. When I came out, satisfied nothing was left behind, I turned to shut and lock the front door. *She* was standing there behind the door! And I swear to you she shut that door SLAM in my face.'

14

The Mysterious Monk at Lacock

This is a story that a lady from Bradford-on-Avon told me. It is about a strange occurrence that happened to her on a visit to Lacock Abbey. She was a widow of around sixty years of age at the time – a very quietly spoken woman, with a gentleness of features – and she lived alone except for her beloved little dog, Bracken.

This is her story:

'A really strange thing happened to me in 1991. It was about two years after I had lost my Bertie. He was a wonderful husband, a wonderful man, you know. He wasn't much of a talker, but he always looked after me. He was always there. I miss him so much still. In fact I'd give anything to hear him say "Do you want a cuppa, love?" again, I really would.

Anyway, after he died I think I went into what they call depression. I cut myself off from our friends. I didn't want to talk to anyone about it. And anyway I don't think a lot of people really knew what to say, death is a difficult subject for most. Some people even avoided me. That is often the way of it. And Bertie and I never had any children, we couldn't you see. Bertie had mumps and became quite sterile; I mean, these days they probably could have helped us, but it just wasn't to be for us. Children would have been a great comfort, as when you have children you never really lose anyone, they live on in their children don't they?

Well, as I said, I was in this terrible kind of depression. I just didn't want to go anywhere. Perhaps just down to the shops and back. And, of course, to take Bracken for his walks. Thank God for Bracken! If it wasn't for the comfort that Bracken gave to me I do wonder if I wouldn't have gone and done something silly to myself.

Well, for some reason I still don't understand, I suddenly got the car out one afternoon in early spring and took a drive to Lacock. Maybe I wondered if the marvellous show of crocuses, snowdrops and early daffodils in the Abbey grounds might cheer me up. Bertie had always loved them so; we had gone together to look at them for many years every single spring. He always said it really was the end of the winter and the dark days when you saw them peeping through. We went no matter what the weather was, and sometimes their delicate colours would be just visible through the frozen snow. But Bertie was right, they heralded spring if anything did. He always said the flowers were like bright jewels, a promise of renewal in the dead of winter. Bertie could be a poetic man, although you might not think so.

So off I set in the car, without Bracken I am afraid, who sulked on the sofa in the sitting room, despite being taken for his walk first and given his usual biscuit treats. It was a very cold day, but there was no snow. The sky was very overcast and grey, and a little fog hung around in patches here and there. I did wonder if it was wise to travel out in it. But I went on, determined to see the flowers; feeling that it might make me feel close to Bertie again.

It was around 2 o'clock when I arrived at the Abbey. Lacock House looked spectacular as usual, even in the grey light. Of course Bertie was never interested in the house, he preferred all of the natural things. He loved best the winding river running through the grounds, and the huge stately trees we would sit under for shade in the summer months.

I paid and then went in through the gates where a stunning patchwork of colour hit my eyes. The spring flowers were in abundance that year. The purples, yellows and whites were dazzling!

After I had had my fill of nature's beauty, I decided to go where the old cloisters were in the decaying Abbey. Few people were around – perhaps not many would brave such a cold day. I sat on a huge stone slab that made a seat, and thought about the times Bertie and I had shared there. I think I might have shed a tear or two. Then, coming towards me, I saw this figure. It had a monk's robe on, and a cowl up over its head. I was startled for a moment, then I remembered that this was a place many religious people came to; why, Bertie and I had seen quite a few monks and nuns walking about in the times we had visited.

I sat still, thinking he would pass me by. But to my surprise he did not. In fact, he came and sat right next to me. He did not turn at first to look at me, but just sat, seemingly gazing ahead. I did not want to disturb his reverie; I thought that maybe he was meditating on his beliefs in such a place, so I sat quiet and still next to him and said nothing.

After a little while he threw back his cowl, revealing a young man of around thirty years of age. He had short dark hair, a straight nose, and, when he turned his face to look at me, the most beautiful brown eyes that seemed full of tenderness. He said nothing at all. His eyes conveyed everything. They seemed to be saying that he somehow understood all of my pain and sorrow in an instant. And, as he looked at me, it did not seem like pity, but a kind of reassurance. And, because of it, despite his being a stranger to me, the floodgates opened and I cried and cried, not able to stop. I sobbed as if my heart would break; something I had not been able to do properly since the loss of my beloved Bertie.

All through my wailing the monk sat very still next to me, conveying understanding and comfort without the need for words. Soon I was able to pull myself together enough to clear my tear-blurred vision and blow my nose with my handkerchief. I then went to turn to the young man to apologise for my outpour. But he was gone! Gone in that instant! It was not possible for any human being to have moved out of sight that fast. Of course, I got up and quickly ran this way and that looking for him; but there was no sign of him anywhere. I even went back and walked around the Abbey grounds just to see if he was anywhere about. But he was gone.

Eventually I returned home. It was such an odd experience, but − stranger still − I felt so much lighter in myself. The black cloud of my depression was at last lifting. When I got indoors I made myself some buttered toast and hot tea and shared it with Bracken. The toast and tea tasted good to me again. When I lost Bertie I had lost all appetite.

I have thought about this experience again and again, and have told a few close friends about it. We have all come to the conclusion that the young man must have been something supernatural. One friend said she wondered if he were an angel. Of course, I have no idea who or what he was, but I do know that from that day onwards I felt healed.

Since then I have been more or less back to my old self. I still do miss Bertie, of course, and I still say goodnight to him every night. But the paralysing grief has gone now. I started to go out again with friends, for a meal, or a game of bingo. Things never will be the same again without my Bertie, but at least I feel I can go on now and still find some joy in life.'

15

Hauntings at Calne

An old man who had lived in the town of Calne all his life, and his family too, for generations, told me the tale of the vicar's daughters. It is a strange account of a lady and her family who moved into one of the cottages near the magnificent St Mary's church in the old section of the town. This part of Calne is full of history and is notable both for its spectacular architecture and for the famous people who once made their homes there. Here, there is a house where Coleridge, the famous poet, lived for a while, he of *The Rime of the Ancient Mariner*. Another house boasts that Joseph Priestley, the man said to have discovered oxygen, once stayed. At one time a great Anglo Saxon palace covered the area that is now The Green and Kingsbury Street. Also, there was once a monastery enclosing the area from Church Street to Castlefields Park. So it is perhaps no wonder there have been stories of strange happenings and sightings in this part of town, so steeped is it in history.

This is the old man's story:

'I were in the church, cleanin' the brasses as usual, when this lady comes right up to me an' starts askin' about the cottage she had just moved into. An' not only that, she taked I right aback and asks me if I believed in ghosts! Well, I didn't know what to answer at fust. But, you know, I always thinks it pays to be truthful, if you can, in any circumstance. In my mind, see, it won't do to tell even a little fib because I do believe it do come right back at ya.

'Er were a pretty little soul, this lady, and 'er 'ad a sweetness of nature with it. So I looks up and says that I believed there were many strange things in this world that couldn't be easily explained away, ghosts bein' one o' them.

"So you do believe?" 'er asked me.

"Well, I can't say that I do not," I replied. I were silent then. I thought that were rather enough to say to a stranger about such a subject. You got to be careful what you tells all and sundry, to my mind.

But she weren't 'avin' none of it. She just went on wi' what she wanted to say. So she says to me, "We moved into the cottage in June this year. Don't get me wrong, we love it there but ..."

"But what?" says I. I knew the very cottage she was talking about. An' I knew what 'er were going to say, or as near as damn it anyway!

"Well," she continued, "just after we had moved in I was stood in the kitchen and I swear that I heard a rustle of skirts. And I could smell a strong scent of lavender. And then, I really honestly thought that something, or someone, had walked past me, you know, I felt the draught from it. Well, me being me, I dismissed it as fancy. I do believe in the supernatural, but I am a realist too. I look for logical explanations first in all things.

This happened, as I said, in June. Then I got so busy that I almost forgot about it; perhaps I wanted to. I had not mentioned this to my family, as my son, who is eight years old, is a very sensitive and impressionable sort of child and I did not think that he would welcome the thoughts of ghosts in our home.

Then, in September, we were all in the sitting room one evening, at around 9 o'clock, and there was a very strong smell of fresh toast. I even asked my husband if he had just made some. But nobody had made any toast. Yet my husband and I and our son could all smell it very distinctly. The cottage has thick walls and we had no windows or doors open, so the smell could not have come from a neighbour's house. Again, we played it down, as we did not want to unduly upset our son. We did not mention it again, despite the fact that we often did smell toast when none was being prepared.

Then, in October, something happened again. I am afraid to say that I had a real tiff with my husband. If we argue I always choose to sleep on the sofa in the living room, as we have no spare bedroom. So I was lying on the sofa in the early hours of the morning, wide awake. I can never get to sleep if my husband and I argue; I always find it too upsetting. I had a book with me, so I had a small lamp on to read by. I really could not concentrate on the book, so I just lay there thinking of the things we had said to one another.

I was lying there, facing the door that leads from the kitchen into the living room, when I saw the handle of the door turn, *as if some invisible hand had opened it.* I just stared in horror and disbelief! I nearly screamed, but managed to stop myself, thinking how it would frighten our son. It was a little while before I had the courage to get up and investigate. Of course, I found absolutely nothing there. I felt like running up and telling my husband, but my pride would not let me after our falling out. So I never did tell him. Anyway, my husband is a man who knows these things exist, but would much rather not talk about them.

Very soon after this episode my son called down to me one night at around 11 o'clock. He sounded a little distressed, so I ran quickly up to his attic bedroom.

'I saw two ladies out there,' he said, pointing out of his window to the passageway that is the approach to our cottage. 'Had they been to a fancy dress party, Mummy?' he asked.

'Are they coming to our house now? They have long dresses on like in the old days, Mummy.'

I looked out of the window, but could see no sign of anyone. It was a moonlit night and I could see our little patio garden quite clearly, and the gate leading to our house. I even ran downstairs and outside, but there really was no one there. I went back in and settled my son down, reading him a story, as this always got him back to sleep again. I told him that perhaps the ladies he had seen had been to a neighbour's party, I did not know what else to say. But he soon settled down again, as children often do, and was quickly asleep.

The next thing that occurred was just before Christmas that year. My mother and father-in-law had come to visit me for a morning coffee and a mince pie. My son had not yet broken up from school. We had been doing renovation work in the kitchen, so it was in a bit of a mess. I got them into the sitting room where it was cosy and closed the door on the draughty kitchen. So we sat and chatted over our coffee on what seemed to be a perfectly normal, if chilly, December morning. I felt quite relaxed as I had finished work for the Christmas period.

Suddenly we all jumped out of our skins. Something had been thrown with real force at the glass door separating the kitchen and the living room. I ran out into the kitchen to find bits of pea gravel everywhere! I swear too that, as I entered, I heard a mischievous giggle somewhere nearby. My in-laws came into the kitchen behind me. They were flabbergasted, to say the least. None of us could make out where the gravel had come from, let alone who might have thrown it. We had no pea gravel anywhere, not even in the garden.

After this incident I decided that I must find out more about the history of the cottage. I soon found out that it had been built in 1830 by the church authorities. Someone told me that there might be more information to be found in this church, St Mary the Virgin, as it is opposite the cottage. I found out that the cottage we lived in had once been one cottage, but now was divided into two. Other than that I didn't gather much more information, not knowing really where to look for it.

Well, a few months later another thing happened. I was up in my son's bedroom cleaning. He was lying face down on his bed, propped up on his elbows, reading.

He quietly looked up from his book and said, 'You don't hum songs to yourself when you are cleaning do you, Mum?'

I laughed at this, saying something to the effect that maybe I did not hum songs as I wasn't ever too happy cleaning, but still, it had to be done. Then he replied, to my amazement, 'The lady who comes in here doing some dusting always hums to herself.'

I put down the books I had retrieved from underneath his bed, before carefully asking him what lady he meant.

'Well, it is one of those ladies I saw out of my window that night,' he said, in a very matter of fact voice. 'You know, I think she might be a ghost.'

I was too dumbfounded to reply, but he went on, 'I am not afraid of her, Mummy, so you have no need to worry. She always smiles at me, and is very pleasant. She seems happy all of the time. She always hums those tunes to herself as she dusts my room.'

Eventually, when I found my voice again, I asked if he had seen her much. He replied that, yes, he had, quite a few times, in fact, and that he did not mind at all. He said he had not mentioned it to me, or to his father, as he feared it might worry us."

So this is what this lady told me, while we stood in the church. So I says to this pretty young woman, I says, "That'll be the vicar's daughters your boy be seein'. That cottage o' theirs were built by their father, the then vicar of this 'ere parish. They lived thur all their lives they did. An' let me tell 'ee this, m'dear, your little 'un aint the fust to see 'em neither. Several that 'as lived thur before you 'ave 'ad similar experiences. Many was frightened right away by it. But I don't think they bring no harm. I think that perhaps they liked livin' thur so much they didn't want to leave, eh?"

Well, 'er seemed satisfied enough by this, and left the church smilin' to 'erself. She an' her family still do live in that thur cottage. So I be thinkin' that they must 'ave got used to 'avin' the vicar's daughters around.'

16

The Yew Tree in Tisbury

This story was told to me by a couple who had a strange experience whilst visiting the small village of Tisbury, not far from Salisbury. This is a quaint and pretty place with fine architecture and a lovely river running through. But there is something else that draws many tourists to Tisbury – it is, of course, the rather amazing yew tree that stands in the churchyard there. This yew is thought to be about 4,500 years old. It is a truly wondrous thing and people come just to gaze on something so incredibly ancient yet still alive. It is indeed awesome, and no one is able to look at it without deep respect.

John and Susan had moved into the area in 1979. Both had lived in Bristol before moving, so they were very glad when they found a little house in Shaftesbury and could become more countrified. At that time their daughter, Arabella, was four years old. Of course, when they started to explore their surrounding area they heard about the ancient tree at Tisbury. They could hardly wait to go and see this tree as it sounded so remarkable, and they wanted their little girl to see something that they considered to be almost magical.

This is their story, told by John:

'It was a really hot day in July; it was my birthday, so we packed a picnic and decided to go to Tisbury for the day. We were all excited at the prospect of seeing the tree, of course, as well as sitting in a shady place to enjoy our meal.

It's not far to Tisbury from where we live, and we were rather glad of it that day as Arabella used to get so tetchy in the heat if she was in the car for long. We got to the village fairly quickly, and we parked and had a look around for a while. But it was so hot that we soon decided to head for the church, which we easily found. The churchyard is pretty and very peaceful. A river meanders through at the back of the church, and there are tall trees that give perfect shade at the water's edge on hot days. We thought it a perfect place to eat our lunch.

Arabella, though, was determined to see the yew tree we had told her about, and ran off around the front of the church, with us in hot pursuit.

We have to say we were in awe of it, despite the fact that it has split with age and has had to be cemented together. But it is still very spectacular and one feels very humble, somehow, to be near something that is still living but of such great antiquity.

Arabella was running around as usual, chattering away, more to herself than anybody. We caught hold of her hand and told her a little bit about the tree, explaining how old it was and saying it was a great-great-great-granddaddy of trees. We are not sure how much she understood of this, but she stood looking up at the tree with wide eyes and then went up and patted the trunk and gave it one of what we call her "knowing looks".

We then returned to our chosen spot at the back of the church, at the river's edge, to have our picnic. It was a truly glorious afternoon; the sun was playing on the water, dazzling our eyes, and swifts were hunting and screaming overhead. Susan lay back on the grass when she had finished eating, lapping up the sun as only a true sun worshipper is able. She closed her eyes and relaxed in the idyllic surroundings. Arabella and I sat and watched the gentle flow of the river for a while but, typically, she could not keep still and ran around the gravestones chatting to Mr Ted, her old battered teddy bear, which had once been loved by her mother and was now loved by her.

There was no one else around and we relaxed in the warmth of the day. Susan seemed to have dozed off and I sat mesmerised by the water. Suddenly I realised that Arabella had gone out of sight. So, panicking a little, I ran round to the front of the church. Sure enough, to my great relief, Arabella was there under the yew tree. Mr Ted had fallen onto the path leading up to the church porch so I went and picked him up.

Arabella did not seem to notice me at all. She was, in fact, seemingly in deep conversation with the tree, or that is what I surmised. I called to her and she came running, blonde ponytail bobbing as she ran. Arabella used to run everywhere; we seldom saw her walk. She then turned before she got to me, and waved in the direction of the tree. By then Susan had appeared, looking slightly perplexed and anxious. I assured her that all was well and soon we were all laughing again in the sunshine. We played a game of tag with Arabella, who screamed with delight every time she was caught.

I had my camera with me, so I took some photos of Susan and Arabella near the tree and at the front of the church. Susan then took some of me with Arabella. Then an elderly couple approached us. They stopped to talk, charmed by Arabella, as most people were. They too had come to see the awesome tree. I asked the elderly gentleman if he would mind taking a family snapshot of Susan, Arabella and me together under the great yew.

He agreed immediately and so we all got under the tree and the old chap took the photograph. We had a job with Arabella as she kept on looking behind her and giggling. I had to explain several times that she was to keep still and look ahead whilst the photo was being taken.

Eventually it was done and the man gave me my camera back. He and his wife said that they hoped that it would be a good picture and that we were a very attractive family. They then left the churchyard.

It was not long after that we decided too that it was time to leave. We all felt relaxed, but the heat was tiring – and even Arabella was slowing down. Just as we passed the yew tree on our way out of the churchyard Arabella waved at the tree and shouted, "Bye, bye." Susan and I smiled at this. Arabella was a strange child; she often talked to flowers and plants, as well as people and animals, so we thought that she must have been talking to the yew tree.

About a week later we had the photographs developed that were taken on that day. We all sat on the sofa to look at the pictures together. They had come out well, lovely views of the pretty churchyard and the river. And one of Susan looking tanned and beautiful, her long blonde hair like a sea of gold around her head as she lay relaxed on the grass. And another of Arabella, Mr Ted under one arm, bending to pick a daisy. And me in the church porch, my trousers looking several sizes too big for me as usual, and my hair never behaving itself, sticking out at all angles.

And then the photograph that the old gentleman had taken, the one of us all together underneath the yew tree …

Susan and I looked in disbelief at one another when we saw this photograph. But it was Arabella who spoke first. She said, "That was a nice man, Daddy." And she pointed to a man in the photograph who was standing behind us all. He was a tall man with a solemn, but kindly, face and shoulder length white hair. Susan took a deep breath and said, "But John there wasn't …"

I knew just what she was about to say – that there wasn't any man behind us on the day that photograph was taken. It would have been impossible for him to stand behind us like that and us not to know. I turned to Arabella. "Did you talk to that man?" I asked, pointing to the figure in the photo. "Oh yes," she answered, "I talked to him, Daddy. But he didn't say anyfink back. But he did keep smiling at me, Daddy. He was very nice.'"

17

The Devil's Den

This story was told to me by a young man called Simon, who was a
student at Bath University in the 1990s when this incident happened.
He had been with a group of friends visiting some of the ancient sites around
Wiltshire, and when the Summer Solstice came round they all decided it
would be fun to camp out overnight somewhere. They knew that there would
be a gathering at Avebury stone circle, but they decided against going there
as occasionally people of dubious intent would turn up and spoil the fun.

Then Lynne, the only girl of their party, decided that she would like to
see a place called the Devil's Den. Sometimes known as Pan's Den, this is
situated on farmland between Fyfield and Marlborough. It is an ancient
burial chamber, but two standing sarsen stones and a capstone are all that
are visible now. It was once described as being 230 ft in length; this was
before 1921, when it was reconstructed, as presumably the stones had
collapsed, and it has remained the same to this day.

There have been many tales concerning the Devil's Den over the years.
One describes a huge animal with saucer-like shining eyes; this animal has
often been seen sitting on top of the capstone. Others have stated that they
have heard mysterious music coming from somewhere in the region of the
upright stones, but when they investigated, found no one and nothing that
could have produced such music.

This is Simon's story:

'It was about 11 o'clock on Summer Solstice Eve, though you would not
have believed it, because that night was blowing a gale. We, that is Lynne,
Danny, Nicolas and I, pulled up in Nic's faithful old banger at a gate
leading to a farm track, just off the main A4 to Marlborough. A rather
disfigured signpost pointed nonchalantly to a rutted track behind the
closed gate. All the letters had been removed from this signpost except for
the V. We did laugh at this, but it also made us wonder if the farmer who
owned the land was a little unfriendly. We were not certain, in fact, that we
had found the right place.

"I am sure this is it," said Lynne, looking at her well-thumbed map. "I
think it has got to be in that direction." At least she was indicating the same

direction that the signpost was suggesting. A flicker of doubt did cross our minds, however, as the post could have been turned round by anybody who saw visitors as unwelcome.

We three guys just looked at her, waiting for other instructions. We had got out of the car and were standing huddled in a group against the wind. We were, unfortunately, mostly dressed for summer weather and had come ill equipped for the change in temperature.

"I can't see any sign of it," protested Danny, looking around at the silhouetted night-time landscape. "I'd rather forget about it myself and head on back to Avebury and sit in the car. It's cold. And I want to roll a fag." I must admit I felt like agreeing with Danny on this. But Lynne was a force to be reckoned with, despite being small and as light as a feather. She looked so frail and yet so determined as she stood there, the wind fiercely tugging at her long brown hair; I just knew that she would not give up easily. So I suggested that perhaps we could go a little way down the track and see if we could get a view of the burial mound. Nic agreed, saying that he could see it meant a lot to Lynne to find this place. Danny looked very cheesed off at this, to say the least.

"Well we have come this far!" said Lynne, jutting out her chin in that purposeful way she had. That did it really. We all knew that when Lynne did that we would be on to a loser. She would get her way, no matter what. So we put on our coats and backpacks and began to battle our way down the rather forlorn farm track against the howling wind. Danny moaned and protested and almost ran back to the car, and probably would have if it were not for the fact that Lynne had followed him. She herded him back to us like a sheepdog, worrying at his heels all the while. Danny did as he was told, but he sulkily said, "I tell you, this place had better be worth it!"

It was getting dark as we trudged on. But, as always at Summer Solstice, the light never seemed to completely leave the sky. So stars shone brightly in a backdrop of azure blue. We seemed to have slogged on for quite a way before Lynne's excited voice shouted, "It's over there! I can see it!" And sure enough, against the skyline, placed in what seemed to be the middle of a field, there were the standing stones, the capstone looming out of the semi darkness – the Devil's Den. It was still some way into the distance and, despite the bitter wind, we all ran towards it. I don't think us lads would have admitted it to Lynne, but once we had caught sight of it, we too were thrilled by the prospect of getting close to the strange and almost mythical burial chamber.

When we got about one hundred yards from it, we all suddenly stopped in our tracks. We could just make out some shapes moving in and out, and around the stones. It was Danny who spoke first. His voice had a high-pitched edge to it. "Wow man! What the Hell?"

We had all instinctively moved closer together in the darkness. "It looks like people of some kind," breathed Nic.

"They look like they have some sort of long robes on," said Lynne. She was intently watching what appeared to be about half a dozen people, or should I say shapes like people, moving around the Devil's Den in a sort of rhythmic way.

"I am outta here," said Danny, turning quickly on his heel.

"No!" said Lynne firmly catching him by the arm. "Let's go across and see what they are up to."

"You joke," said Nic.

"Don't think she's joking, Nic," I said.

We all stood there for a while, irresolute, just gazing at the erect stones with the capstone, the Devil's Den. And how sinister it had suddenly become! Now the figures seemed to be moving in a circular motion around the stones. Then we heard a sound that can only be described as chanting. Deep and sonorous, it sent shivers up my spine.

The figures seemed to take on an almost ethereal appearance. I really don't believe that any of us could have said if they were real or not. They moved as if they were now performing some odd kind of dance; a spiral dance. Round and round they went, chanting all the while. No words could be distinguished, only the low hum of the voices in the distance. Then, as if they had suddenly noticed our presence, the figures seemed to melt into the monument, or somewhere nearby – and completely disappeared.

Lynne was the first to start running towards the chamber. I followed close behind. Danny and Nic just stood still where they were, apparently rooted to the spot. I saw Lynne running around the monument. "They have gone!" she was shouting. "Gone! Can you believe it!"

Danny and Nic had found their legs and had joined us. "Look," said Danny, "let's just get the Hell out of here." I could see in the semi-darkness that his face was very white and drawn.

"Where could they have gone, and so quickly?" Lynne asked breathlessly as she joined us.

"I think you are the only one who cares where they have gone," said Nic, looking very uneasy.

"Do you think they were witches?" asked Lynne.

"Witches. Ghosts. Ghouls. Goblins. Like Nic said, who cares? I just want to go," Danny's voice was very strained.

Then Nic and Danny waited no longer. We saw them running as if for their lives, back towards where the car was parked. Lynne and I soon followed. When we were all in the car and safely driving away, we speculated on what we had seen, and of course came to no reasonable conclusion. Danny would not even talk of it.

I think, on reflection, that we all did witness something very strange that night. But none of us could tell what it was we had really seen and heard. I can only say that if the shapes were not spectres, then they did have an extraordinary ability to melt into the surrounding countryside, as we were sure no one had left the monument. Some people have since told me that witches have the ability to do this, but I am inclined to think that a little far fetched.

But there again, I used to think that everything supposedly supernatural was a bit far fetched …'

18

The Lady with the Golden Earrings

This story was told to me by my husband. He is inclined to be a rather rational man, and has what might be described as a logical mind. But when he was nine years old he experienced something for which he could find no logical explanation. The events took place in the town of Trowbridge in the 1960s.

This is his story:

'I can remember the house as if it were yesterday. It was an old Victorian town house with three storeys, rather bleak and dark looking, in Harford Street. Dad had rented it for us to stay in whilst he was doing another one of his renovation jobs on our proper home. He was always doing up properties; it was his business.

Anyway, we moved into this house, Mum and Dad, my two brothers and me. I am not sure that I was ever entirely happy about us going there, not even from the beginning, but it was dismissed when I mentioned it, as these things often are. However, nothing untoward happened for some time after moving in. But then, perhaps this was just because we were all so very tired after the move. I think that we were all asleep most nights as soon as our heads hit the pillow.

It must have been a month or so after actually arriving there that the first incident happened. I remember being woken by my five-year-old brother Stephen, who had crawled into bed beside me. It was around midnight and I wondered what on earth was going on, as he had never done this before. I then realised that he was shaking with fear.

I thought at first that maybe he had had a nightmare and, as we had to share a bedroom, the obvious thing would be to come to me. It was really only a two-bedroom house, so we were a little overcrowded. There was an attic on the third floor, but it had looked so empty and unwelcoming, and so full of cobwebs, that none of us had wanted to sleep in there.

Stephen lay next to me, trembling still. He was holding the covers up over his head, as if desperate not to look out. I asked him again and again what was wrong, but I could get nothing from him at all; he just lay there, trembling and silent. After about half an hour I asked him again. I wanted him to return to his own bed. I was tired and needed to sleep. At this he actually screamed, "No! No! No!" He was adamant that he would not go back to his own bed. I was getting rather fed up by now, despite his obvious discomfort. I felt that it might help if he explained what it was all about. So I decided to go and tell Mum and Dad, even though I knew that they would be displeased to be woken in the middle of the night, as they both had work the next day.

Mum followed me back to our room. She was in a pink quilted dressing gown, and she looked rather disgruntled at being woken. She marched over to my bed, pulled the covers off Stephen's head and asked him what was wrong, whilst trying not to wake Gary, our littlest brother at eighteen months, who was still sound asleep in his cot. Stephen still would not say anything. But Mum persuaded him that he had been dreaming and put him back in his own bed. I climbed under the covers again and was very soon fast asleep.

I really did not think much more about the incident. In the days that followed I played football with the other kids in the street after school and went fishing down on the canal, in other words did all that was usual for kids back then. Family life went on as normal; we all slept well, and nothing was mentioned about that night at all by anyone.

Then, one Saturday night – I remember it being Saturday, as I was always allowed to stay up to watch *Match of the Day* with Dad on Saturday nights. It was a real treat and I always felt kind of special, as it was only me, being the eldest, that was allowed to do so. So, on this Saturday, my two brothers were asleep when I crept into the bedroom and got into bed. I had not been in bed too long and was just dozing off, half thinking, half dreaming, about being able to play a ball like George Best. Then, suddenly, Stephen was yet again climbing into my bed. And worse still, Gary was now awake too, and crying.

"Have you been dreaming again, Steve?" I asked. Mum and Dad were now both in bed. I didn't relish the prospect of waking them. Stephen would not answer me. He just pulled the covers up over his head and lay there shivering. But Gary, who only had a few words, was pointing towards the half open bedroom door, and plainly said, "Yady." I couldn't make out what he was talking about, as I could see no lady of any kind; we did not even have a picture on the wall with a lady on it.

I gave up, and tried to get Stephen back to his own bed. We always had a low-wattage bulb lighting up the landing and the bedroom door was ajar, so it was never dark in our room. So I tried to soothe Stephen and Gary by saying that there really was no need to get upset by dreams, and that we always had a light on anyway. But Stephen just shivered and shook, and then eventually got the words out, "*She* was here again!"

"She?" I asked.

"The lady with the golden earrings," Stephen almost whispered the words.

I was trying to take this in whilst watching Gary, who was now playing with the coloured beads that ran along the top rail of his cot. He, at least, seemed to have settled down a bit.

I decided to assure Stephen that he had only been dreaming again and that Gary had picked up on his distress. He eventually got back into his own bed and fell sound asleep. Gary, too, had fallen asleep, thumb in mouth, on the top of his covers. I went across and pulled them over him. As I did so I thought that I glimpsed something out of the corner of my eye. A flash of green, right by the open bedroom door. I ran as quietly as I possibly could, and went out onto the landing. The light was on as usual and there was nothing to be seen. But I had the distinct feeling that someone, or something, *had* been there.

Suddenly I pulled myself together, thinking how catching it could be once someone had started the fear ball rolling. I went quietly back to bed. Gary and Stephen remained asleep.

I wasn't able to get to sleep very well after this, I tossed and turned for what seemed an age before I decided that it was probably better to have a read for a while. So I picked up my *Shoot* annual and started to read by torchlight.

I think I must have dozed off, for I remember waking with a start and seeing that my alarm clock said 1 o'clock. I think that I also heard some sort of noise. Perhaps I didn't. I really don't know. But I looked up, and there in the doorway was a woman. She looked very real. She had dark hair pulled back from her face and fixed in a bun. She had a long green dress on and some sort of shawl around her shoulders. But what I noticed the most was her shiny hooped gold earrings – they seemed to catch the light from the landing. She just stood there and seemed to be looking at me, and my sleeping brothers.

I lay there, looking back at her like one hypnotised. I felt afraid, but very curious at the same time. Then she turned and walked off onto the landing. I quickly got out of bed, intent on following her. I don't know why I did that. Perhaps I thought that she might lead me somewhere? Perhaps I wanted to prove to myself that she was really a ghost, just as I had feared?

Well, anyway, I followed her. I saw her going up the stairs leading to the attic and I ran after her; she seemed almost to float along the ground at some speed.

When I opened the door to the attic room there was no sign of her. I switched on the only light, a bulb hanging from the centre of the ceiling. Frills of cobwebs were everywhere. The room felt very cold and, of course, was completely empty. I suddenly felt very uneasy in there, and I quickly shut the door. As I left I swear I heard footsteps in that room. But I did not have the courage to open the door again and look inside.

We moved house not long after this. I cannot say that either me or my brothers were sorry to leave that house. Mum and Dad had laughed when I told them what I had seen, saying that I had too vivid an imagination. Stephen and Gary would say nothing on the subject. But we all knew that we had seen her, the lady with the golden earrings. And years later we can still remember it. We were all so young at the time that she had really scared us. If we had been older, we would probably have tried to find out a little more about her. But perhaps that just wasn't to be. But one thing is for sure, we all saw her perfectly clearly, and she must have been a ghost.'

19

The Little Ghost Dog of Marlborough

This tale was told to me by a lady who lived in an old cottage in Marlborough. She and her husband had moved there in the 1980s with their young son and had done much renovation work, including building a new extension onto the back of the house.

This is her story:

'We were all really relieved when we were able, at last, to move into our cottage. It had been a bit of a difficult time really. For about eighteen months we had been living in a small, cramped caravan hardly big enough for one, let alone three.

It was a sunny but cold day in March when we moved everything in. Friends came around to give us a hand and help lug the heavier stuff, and to take turns in keeping on eye on Gerald, our little boy, who was then three. Of course, Gerald was running everywhere and getting into everything, just as any healthy youngster might. He was overwhelmed with the fact that he had now got so much space – and a garden! So he was even more lively than usual.

It was not until later on that day, when our friends had left, and Barrie, my husband, had gone to get a well-earned takeaway, that Gerald started to say things. I was in the sitting room unpacking some ornaments when he ran in, his face beaming, and shouted, "Doggie!"

I followed him into the kitchen, thinking that perhaps a neighbour's dog had strayed in. But there was no dog to be seen. I looked at Gerald, who was now playing on the floor with a toy tractor. He was an imaginative child, and he loved dogs. He was always cuddling any dog that would let him. I wondered to myself if it was time we got him a puppy. Barrie and I both loved dogs, and I was only thinking how it is good for children to be brought up around them. Having a garden now made it a perfect idea. Well, we would have to wait a bit to settle in, then perhaps it would be the right time to get a puppy.

I thought no more of any of this in the next few days; they were very busy, as they always are when you have just moved house. One morning, I was up in the bathroom, which is on the second floor, when I heard Gerald, who was downstairs, screaming and laughing, just the way he did when he was at playgroup with other children. I ran down to see what it was he was having so much fun with. He came running up to me, eyes all bright, and said, "Doggie hungry." He led me into the kitchen and pointed to the fridge.

"He wants food. Doggie does."

"What doggie, love?" I asked, looking around. I wondered if he had one of his many toy dogs there with him, but I couldn't see one.

Gerald frowned to himself. "Oh, he gone now!" he said, a little disappointedly. But as it always was with Gerald, he forgot about it all and ran out into the garden to ride his bike.

I soon forgot about it, too. And before long spring had flown into summer and we were all busy doing odd jobs and tidying the garden. Gerald loved it. He was a child who could amuse himself most of the time. I often saw him in the garden, through the kitchen window, chattering away to himself for all he was worth. I must admit that it did look at times uncannily as if he were talking to someone, or something, else. But, I decided, that is children for you!

Then, one hot day in June, Gerald came up to me as I was weeding in the garden, and said, "Shall we keep doggie, Mummy? He is nice. I like his long ears."

"What are you talking about, Gerald? What doggie?" I was half annoyed at him for starting on about the dog again.

"That doggie, of course, Mummy," he was pointing towards the back door. He began to giggle as if he could see something doing something funny.

Then it dawned on me that it was obviously a game. "Mummy can't see him," I said. "Perhaps he is hiding?"

"Don't be silly, Mummy. He isn't hiding," Gerald replied emphatically. "He is running about." He giggled again, looking towards the back door.

I just got on with my weeding. It was obvious that Gerald had an imaginary friend who happened to be a dog. It was, perhaps, the time to go and get him a real pet.

That evening, as I was putting Gerald to bed, I broached the subject, and asked him if he wanted a real puppy to play with. I thought that he would be really excited at the prospect of this, but he contemplated it, head on one side, like a little cock sparrow, before answering.

"Will the doggie that already lives here like another doggie here?" he asked, carefully.

"Oh yes," I replied, not wishing to ruin the game. "Doggies always like each other's company. So I am sure he'll be all right about it."

"Good," said Gerald, apparently satisfied. "He is a nice doggie, Mummy. He is brown and white, and has long ears."

"Oh, that's nice," I said, rather lamely.

I then began to read him his usual bedtime story. It always had to be Pooh Bear or Paddington, both of which he loved. Soon I saw that he was dozing off. The curtains were drawn, but, because it was high summer, the room was still quite light. I went to creep away, when I caught something on the periphery of my vision that made me stop dead. I turned and saw what I can only describe as a sort of indentation in the bedcover. And I could have sworn that it looked as if there were something invisible trying to make itself comfortable on the bed. The way a cat or dog will turn round and around before settling down to sleep. Whatever it was it seemed to want to lie right next to Gerald. I was frozen to the spot with fear. I really did not know what to do next.

Then, Gerald stirred in his sleep, half opened his eyes and, looking down to the thing on the bed, gave one of his bright smiles and said, "Hello doggie." And then promptly dropped off back to sleep again.

I left the room, shutting the door behind me and leaning against it for some time, trying to compose myself. My hands were sweating, and my heart pounding loudly in my chest. I wished that Barrie were there with his no nonsense Northern sense. I took a deep breath and opened the door again to peer at Gerald. He was still fast asleep, looking like a miniature angel, blond hair against the pillow, dark lashes touching his soft creamy cheeks. Everything appeared normal. The bedcover was slightly rucked where Gerald had obviously moved around in his sleep. But there was now no sign of the indentation that I had thought that I had seen.

I left Gerald asleep and went downstairs to make myself a cup of tea, wishing I had something stronger in the house. I decided to go and out and do something that was "normal". I took a gardening trowel and began to plant out some geraniums. As I did this I began to think to myself that I was getting as overactive an imagination as my son! Perhaps it was catching? I laughed out loud to myself at the thought.

Then, the old man who lived next door peeped over the fence. "Nice evenin'," he said.

I smiled in return and we chatted a while. I was quite glad of the company. He got round to talking about the cottage we lived in, and about its previous owners. He told me that there was a local baker in the town about thirty years back; and that this baker and his wife had lived in our cottage. He said they had no children, the baker and his wife, but they did have a little liver and white spaniel they had doted on. He said that it was a nice dog. It loved children, and would play with his youngsters every chance it got. It was always escaping through the fence to get to them. After our neighbour had gone I pondered on what he had said. A little spaniel dog, liver and white. Spaniels have long ears …

We eventually did get a terrier pup. And the funny thing is, this little pup would go out into the garden to play, and sometimes it would look for all the world like he was actually playing a rough and tumble game with another dog. And Gerald would scream with laughter and say, "You were right, Mummy. The doggies do like each other!'"

20

Accident on the Swindon Road

Sam, a retired man from Swindon, told me this story. It happened in 1971. Sam, who then lived in Swindon, had decided to do a little taxi driving after his retirement as a lorry driver, to prevent boredom and to help support his meagre old age pension. His wife had died several years previously, and so, with no one at home to worry about, he often did late night taxi work.

This is his story:

'It was right near Christmas when something happened I shall never forget. It was a cold and inhospitable night. Sleet was falling fast in the headlamps of the car I was driving. I really felt, for once, that I would be glad to get back home to Swindon. I had the heater on and it was warm, but I could see that the weather might take a turn for the worse.

I had a fare to take to Wroughton. It turned out to be three young, and rather sozzled, RAF blokes. Still their company had been cheery, if a little noisy, and they had given me a rather generous tip, so I was in quite a good frame of mind, despite the weather.

It was around 12.30 am that I started to head back along the road from Wroughton to Swindon. The sleet was falling heavier by now, making visibility more and more difficult. I really was glad to be on my way home.

I had just left the town of Wroughton when I saw a young man walking along the pavement, thumbing a lift. He was dressed only in a tee shirt and jeans. As I got nearer I could see that he couldn't have been any more than about twelve years of age. There were no houses nearby on this particular bit of the route, and the road there is quite fast and dangerous. So, due to the fact that this boy had not even got a coat in such weather and the danger of where he was walking in the dark at that time of night, I did a thing which, of course, taxi drivers are not supposed to do, I stopped to offer him a free lift. Thoughts went through my mind of my own grandchildren tucked up warm and safe in bed; this boy was about the same age as one of them.

I signalled, and pulled in alongside him. I could see that I had been right, he was about twelve years old. He was slightly built, and quite tall for his age. His skin was very, very pale and I feared that the cold outside could have had something to do with it. I hoped that I would not startle him.

"Hello," I said, as cheerfully as I could, trying to imply that I wasn't a weirdo or anything, but just an old granddad. "It's a terrible night young man. You must be cold. Where is your coat?"

He did not answer me at all. He just stood and looked at me. I wondered if he was afraid, me being a stranger and all. But he did not really have a scared look about him.

"Don't worry, lad. I'm really okay. You can even have a talk with me old boss on the CB if you like. Would you care for a lift? No charge to young men with no income as yet. Do you live in Swindon?"

He nodded. He still stood there, not moving, the sleet falling all around him.

"Old Town or what?" I asked.

He nodded again.

"Old Town it is! Hop in, lad." I got out and opened the back door for him. He got straight in and I shut the door.

As I pulled off I could see him in my mirror, sitting there on the back seat, looking straight ahead.

"You been out with friends?" I asked. He nodded again. He certainly wasn't much of a conversationalist

"You want to make sure that you take a coat next time." I remember turning up the heater as it seemed that the temperature was dropping rapidly.

Again, he didn't answer me. He just smiled. He certainly seemed a strange and silent young fellow. Odd for his age. My grandchildren were always chatter, chatter, chattering!

Up ahead, peering through the falling sleet, I could see that police warning signs had been put out to slow the traffic. "Dear, oh dear," I said, "looks like there been an accident here earlier. Always at Christmas, eh?" The boy remained silent and passive in the back of the car. He was certainly an easy passenger.

"By God, it is cold!" I said. It seemed strange. The heater was full blast, and I am not a one for feeling the cold normally. We had slowed right down to almost a standstill by now. But at least the traffic ahead was still on the move.

"Looks like they have cleared the road anyways," I said, and turned my head to look at the boy. But to my utter astonishment he was gone! I could not believe it. I hadn't heard him get out of the car. No click of the door shutting, nothing.

I quickly signalled and pulled over. I got out of the car. There was no one to be seen anywhere. Just the traffic, now speeding up a bit and going by. The police danger signs were in place. No police were there any more. The sleet turned into huge flakes of snow. I stood as they hit me softly like a very cold eiderdown, still unable to think where the young boy could have gone. All that I could do was get back into the car and drive home.

When I started driving I had to turn the heater off as it no longer seemed cold. I put it down to the fact that it always warms up a little before it really snows.

As soon as I got home I made a cup of chocolate. I couldn't stop thinking about the boy, and wondering if he was all right. I even thought of calling the police, but I worried that it might bring him trouble if I did. So in the end I went to bed, and tossed and turned until eventually I slept.

That week I just got on with things, despite the mystery of the boy playing on my mind. Luckily it was a very busy time, being Christmas, with taxi bookings for parties and dinners. I was often late to bed. And, being so wide awake from working, could not sleep.

One night, soon after the incident, I had insomnia, so I went downstairs and made a cuppa, and then took it and the local newspaper back up to bed to read. I got into bed and put on my reading glasses, hopeful that a little light reading would make my eyes droop soon enough.

When I looked at the front page I was stunned. There was a picture of the spot where the accident had occurred on the night I had given the young lad a lift. And, as an insert, there was a picture of the young boy himself, the very one I had given the lift to. My heart turned somersaults. Oh my God, I thought, the poor little fellow must have been hit after leaving my taxi! It said a hit and run accident. I felt queasy.

Then, pulling myself together a bit, I read more thoroughly. It said that the boy, aged twelve, was hit by a car whilst crossing the road. The driver who hit him had not stopped. No one was thought to have witnessed the accident. The boy had been found by another motorist. He was already dead before the arrival of the emergency services. Police were appealing for witnesses. The approximate time of the accident was 10 pm. My head swam. How could it have happened at 10 pm?

When I got to work next day, bleary eyed from lack of sleep, many people were talking about the accident as they had read about it in the local paper too. One of my colleagues had a brother in the police force. He was saying how terrible it was, and how no one had come forwards to own up.

I asked him if the accident had been at 10 pm for sure. He assured me that it was. His brother had been one of the first policemen to arrive on the scene.

I told no one about my experience, not knowing what to think of it myself really. Then, I decided that I couldn't keep it to myself any more, as it was troubling me. So I talked to an old friend of my late wife, a lady called Eileen.

Eileen went very quiet when I told her my story. Then, when I had finished, she turned to me and laid a hand on my arm. Looking me in the eyes, she said, "Sam, I know you are not a one for believing in these things, but I truly believe it was the ghost of that young lad that got into your taxi."

I thought about his pale, wan face. I thought about how silent the lad had been. I thought about how cold it had become in my taxi when he was in there … And, at last, I had to come to the same conclusion as Eileen.'

21

The Strange Happenings at Bloomsbury Hall

This is a really terrifying tale told to me by a middle-aged couple who had bought a rather handsome, gothic looking, old country house in the Warminster area. Bloomsbury Hall is not, in fact, the real name of the property. I was specifically asked not to name it in case the new owners were overwhelmed with sightseers.

The couple, whom we shall call Terry and Ruth, had both been in business for most of their lives. Ruth had decided to retire early. Her husband Terry was an art renovator and so was quite happy to move from London at Ruth's request, as all that he needed for his work was a suitable room and storage space. Ruth's dream was to retire to the countryside. After much research, she found what she thought was their dream home in the county of Wiltshire.

This is their story as Terry told it:

'We could not believe it when we found that Bloomsbury Hall was for sale. My wife, Ruth, had found it on the internet on one of the estate agents' sites. It was very impressive. An old six-bedroomed country house made out of Bath stone with high gothic windows, it was set in an acre and a half of mature gardens and had two large outhouses that had once been stables. It was what we were looking for, and much more. The price was, admittedly, a little higher than we had planned to pay. But after we had gone to Wiltshire and viewed it we knew that we just had to own it. Ruth, in particular, fell head over heels for the place. We decided that it was probably the place we would move to and never move again. The only drawback as far as I was concerned was the fact that to the north of the property there was a small church and a churchyard full of Victorian graves. So one had this rather sombre view from the windows on that side of the house. Ruth laughed at my pointing this out. She could not think why I might object to that; she insisted that the church and churchyard were rather quaint and very pretty.

So we went ahead and bought the property. We moved into the house in September 1977. We were over the moon at being able to purchase such a place, and Ruth was already very much in love with it. She said that it would be our forever home – quite a statement, as we had moved many times in our working lives.

Ruth spent many days, after the move, placing our personal things around the house. She spent many more days measuring for curtains and choosing rugs. She had never looked so happy and I had never seen her put so much effort into homemaking before. Being cynical, I did wonder if all this would pall with Ruth. She was, after all, used to concentrating on business, and had spent so little time ever doing anything else. But no, she was fully occupied with the house and garden, and she seemed to be really enjoying her new found freedom from work in the commercial world. She was never bored, as I had feared that she might be. We managed to get a good local chap who helped with the large garden, and a lady who came to do a little cleaning in the house. Ruth and I would sit for hours in the library looking at the plans she had drawn up herself for the garden, or choosing what colour schemes we might prefer for the rooms. So, all in all, we seemed to be living an idyllic existence, in an idyllic place.

Then, in October, I had to go back up to London for a few days. I wanted Ruth to ask one of her friends to stay whilst I was away; I did not think it would be a good idea for her to be on her own, as the house was in a quite remote place. But she absolutely refused, saying that she would really love to be in the house alone, and to be able to have that kind of quietude after the hustle and bustle of London. I knew it would be impossible for me to change her mind. Ruth is one of those people who can suffer from tunnel vision and, besides, people who had worked with her called her 'The Iron Lady'. So I dutifully left for London without argument.

I was very busy with important clients the first day that I was away, but I phoned Ruth at around midday and she seemed relaxed and content. In fact, she said that she was enjoying the peace and quiet and had done some reading, and even a little sewing.

On the second day that I was away we talked on the phone at lunchtime. Ruth told me that she was going shopping. She was excited about getting some more things for the house. I told her to call me later on that evening. She promised that she would. But I got caught up in a dinner date with a client, and so it was 11 o'clock by the time I got back to the friend's house where I was staying. I was told that Ruth had tried to call me half an hour ago.

I immediately phoned her, thinking that she wished to bid me goodnight. We always did this if we were apart for any reason. The phone seemed to be ringing for ages, which put me on edge. Eventually, to my relief, Ruth answered. But her voice seemed very strained.

"The electric seems to have gone off," she said.

"What!" I said, alarmed.

"Yes, Terry, the electric has gone off. I am in the library. I have lit some candles."

"Have you checked the fuse box? Look ..." My mind was working overtime. "Never mind the fuse box. Call the police, love. Put the phone down and do it now."

"But Terry ..."

My heart was thudding now. I felt afraid at my own thoughts. I was really fearful that somebody had done this to be able to break into the house. And she was totally alone.

"You think there might be burglars?" I could hear that her mouth had gone dry.

"Darling. Don't take any chances. Just phone the police. Now. Then call me back." I was cursing myself for letting her stay in the house alone.

"I'll call them right away, Terry." Her voice at least sounded relieved that she could take control of the situation a little.

I put the phone down and waited for her to ring back. I was biting my fingers. I felt sick. The phone eventually rang again, making me start.

"Terry ..." It was Ruth, but it hardly sounded like the Ruth that I knew. The voice had a real edge of fear.

"The police will not be long, love. You have called them?" was all that I could think of to say. I was beside myself, but trying to sound calm to Ruth.

"Terry. I don't think it is burglars."

"What do you mean?"

"It seems to be in here ..."

"What does? What does, Ruth?" I stood up, frantic.

"I don't know ... *Something does* ..."

What she was saying now terrified me. "Ruth, listen. Darling, the police will be there soon. Ruth, can you actually see anybody?"

"Terry, I can't see anybody. But I feel something's in here. Oh God! Oh God, the candles are going out one by one! Terry I will be in the dark soon! I must re-light them!"

I could hear her put down the phone, then her frantic breathing and the click of a lighter. I heard her sob and she kept on saying, "Oh no! Oh no!" When she picked up the receiver again, she was crying. "It is pitch dark,

Terry. It is completely dark in here. Oh, Terry, I can't re-light the candles! Every time I do they are extinguished …"

"How can that be? Ruth, for God's sake, is there anybody in the room with you?"

"I don't know." She was whispering now. Sweat dripped off my brow, my hands were sliding about on the receiver.

"Ruth. Please. Do you think there is someone in the room with you?"

"No. *Something.*"

I took some deep breaths. Perhaps she was getting jittery about nothing. It was my only hope. "Try and re-light the candles," I said. I was so frantic I was babbling.

I heard her put the phone receiver down again, and then the click of the lighter. She picked up the receiver again. "I've managed to light a candle, Terry. I can't see anyone in the room."

I was trembling. "Thank God for that!"

"The room has such an eerie feel. I don't know why I am so afraid, Terry. I don't think it's burglars."

"Hang on in there, love. The police are bound to arrive soon." Tears ran down my face.

"Oh my God, Terry, the candle has been extinguished again!" She was sobbing uncontrollably. This was not at all like Ruth and I realised that she was scared half out of her wits.

All I could reply was, "Oh, Ruth."

Then, I heard a sigh of relief. "The police have arrived. I saw their lights on the drive."

I was so relieved I almost felt that I would die. I brushed away the tears, and the sickness in the pit of my stomach subsided a little. "Go and let them in, Ruth. Get them to check everything. And phone Elenor. She's only forty-five minutes away. Get her to come and stay with you. I won't have you stay alone another minute! Call me back when the police have finished. Get them to stay until Elenor arrives. Make sure that you do."

Soon after midnight our friend Elenor rang to tell me that Ruth was in shock. She had put her to bed with a stiff brandy and would sit with her all night. She told me that the police had found nothing untoward. They had searched the whole house and the grounds. They did find that the trip switch had blown, and soon had the electricity back on. The police had implied that Ruth's imagination had got the better of her when the electricity went off. They obviously did not know Ruth, as Elenor so rightly commented. She was not a woman to get frightened over trifles. Elenor asked me what I thought had really happened. I could not give her an answer.

After this event Ruth did not seem to be able to get back to her old self. She would hardly speak of the incident, but I could tell that it had left a profound mark on her. She told me that she had no answers for what had happened that night. I did not press her. I thought that it might be the best thing to try and put it behind us. I decided that never again would I leave her alone in the house at night. She now seemed to have a definite reluctance to enter the library, and I could understand that. Soon, though, due I think to her resilient nature, she seemed to rally round and was almost herself once more.

We started to lead a busy life again. I thought it would be good for Ruth, so we did a lot of socialising. We went to an amazing Hallowe'en party in London with friends. We went to the theatre, and saw some of the West End shows. In fact, we almost overdid it all in an attempt to erase that awful night from our memories. Soon Ruth seemed back to normal and was planning a Christmas dinner party at the Hall for our friends. I was thankful to see her looking so well and vital again. I settled back down to work, and that frightful night was fading from my memory.

Then, one day early in December, a rather dank sort of day, with thin fog and a drizzle of rain, found me in the garden looking to see if anything else needed clipping back for the winter. Most of the plants had been finished off by the early frosts and the garden was looking a bit dilapidated. The holly bushes seemed to be the only things glowing with life – a deep green shine and fiery berries.

I was on the north side of the house, which overlooked the churchyard. The church seemed to remain mostly unused, except for an occasional service that few seemed to attend. The churchyard itself was never used for burial. It looked a little forlorn in the grey light, the graves all overgrown and unkempt.

My eye was caught by a passing blackbird who stopped to take a holly berry. When I looked up again I thought I saw a figure standing in the churchyard amongst the graves. But I decided that it must have been a trick of the light because when I looked again, it was gone. I remember thinking to myself just how easy it is to see things that were not there on such an eerie day; with the dank grey light possibly playing tricks on the eye.

I decided to dispel any strange feelings by going inside to make hot tea and crumpets for Ruth and me to enjoy. I thought that there certainly was nothing like a good pot of Assam and some buttered crumpets to rid us of the leaden atmosphere of a dismal December day! Of course, I did not mention any of this to Ruth. The last thing I wanted was to revive any memories of that ghastly night, about which we never now spoke. So we cheerfully set about our feast and enjoyed it thoroughly, after which I went and did some work, leaving Ruth to her lists and plans for the Christmas party.

After dinner that evening, a wonderful Beef Wellington that Ruth does so very well, washed down with good Bordeaux, we felt very replenished and relaxed. So relaxed, in fact, that we retired to the library to have coffee. I had lit a cheery fire to dispel any gloom; the logs crackled and sang. It was the first time we had settled in the library since that night. It was actually a magnificent room, oak panelled, with high leaded windows. I was quite determined that we should both enjoy this wonderful room again, so we settled into the red leather chairs with our coffee and stared at the fire. We were both very tranquil, and I fell to wondering if I should have a Cognac to follow.

I do not know which one of us it was that started out of our reverie first. I think that it might have been Ruth. I looked up suddenly to meet her eyes; they were wide with fear.

"What was that?" She was frowning, her body quite taut in her chair. I shook my head. I, too, had thought that I had heard something outside. "Maybe a fox or something in the garden?" I was trying to show that I was calm. Despite my trying we were both leaning forwards in our chairs, listening intently. I could hear it clearly now. A sort of tapping; or was it best described as a scratching noise?

"It is coming from the window!" Ruth's voice faltered.

"It is probably a bird." Despite my efforts, my voice had an edge to it. I got up and went towards the window. For some reason my heart began to pound loudly in my chest. My eyes darted to the telephone, as I wondered if there was someone out there trying to get in.

Ruth, meanwhile, was out of her chair and cautiously going over to the window herself. When she got close she let out a scream. I ran to her quickly.

"What is it, Ruth? What is it?" I looked out of the window and I could just see a figure disappearing through the fog towards the churchyard.

Ruth was panting, and holding her chest. "Oh my God! Oh my God!" was all she could say.

I ran to the telephone and called the police. Ruth's face was like parchment. She was visibly shaking. "Terry. That face! Oh my God, that face!"

I turned to her. "You saw who it was? That is good news. Tell the police the description."

She was shaking her head emphatically. "Terry, Terry …" her voice trembled, "that face was not human."

"Not human?" An echo was all that I could manage.

She swallowed hard, and licked her lips before replying. "It … it was like a living corpse, Terry."

I just looked at my wife in utter astonishment. Words failed me.

"It looked like it was … it looked like it was trying to scratch the lead out of the window-pane."

"What?" I asked, rather stupidly.

"Terry, if it managed to get the lead out, it would have been able to reach its hand in and unlock the window!"

I shook my head. "Ruth, there has to be some logical explanation."

"I saw something really horrible out there, Terry. You know me too well to think that I am a fanciful person."

I could not doubt her. Her fear was more than evident. Our conversation was halted as the police arrived. Two officers immediately climbed out of their car, and one took a flashlight to examine the garden. The other was ringing our doorbell. I went outside and walked around with them. Ruth followed us, far too scared to be left alone in the house. All was quiet, cold and dark. Nothing untoward was visible. There were no footprints by the library window. The police were very thorough.

Soon we went back inside and I made a pot of tea. Ruth told the police that she had definitely seen a face at the window. She did not mention what it looked like. I understood why she felt uneasy about telling them this. The police informed us that it would be best if we set up some lights outside, and saw to it that the house in general was made more secure. Soon they were leaving. I followed them out to their car and thanked them for arriving so promptly. Then, one of the officers, the older of the two, said that similar things had happened to a previous owner of the house. There had been calls about an intruder, although no evidence of a break-in had ever been found. He seemed to be trying to convey something to me, without actually saying it. He finished by telling us that someone would be round to take fingerprint evidence on the library window in the morning, and he said that we were to call at any time if we were at all worried. He was very pleasant.

The days that followed were nightmarish. Ruth could not settle in the house at all any more. She was still insistent about what she had seen. No footprints, no fingerprints, nothing could be found. Ruth was so jittery that it made me feel that way too. I longed to put her mind at rest; but could find no way to do it.

One day, sitting in our bedroom, she described to me exactly what she had seen that night at the window. She said it was tall and skeletal, with yellowing skin covering a bony face. A little bit of wispy hair remained on the skull-like head. And the eyes … Well, Ruth swore that the eyes were just like red glowing coals. She could not get the image from her mind. She soon began to lose weight, and could not rest properly, nor sleep. Her nerves were beginning to be in tatters.

By the time that January came around it was obvious that we would have to sell up. Nothing else untoward had happened. But it was more than apparent by now that quite enough already had. Ruth looked terrible. She was far too thin, and there were dark rings under her eyes. She was a shadow of the woman I knew. The house had become a place where we could find no peace. I was so stressed that I could hardly work.

Eventually, defeated, we accepted a flat to rent from a friend back in London. We put the house up for sale and let the agent deal with it. Ruth was in agonies about the fact that the new owner should be told. I could not let her do this as I thought that we would never sell the house if she did. Even though I knew myself to be sensible on this, I did have a pang of conscience about it for a long time after.

We didn't hear any more about Bloomsbury Hall after it was sold. The new owners stayed there, and are still there, as far as I am aware. Ruth and I often look at photographs of the house and feel so sad that the house we thought was a dream turned out to be a nightmare. We are both still glad we made the decision to move from there. Ruth has picked up again now, and is back working, as I am myself. We both have times when we think about the strange and ghoulish happenings. They will be forever etched on our memories.'

22

The Ghostly Horse at Waylands Smithy

Waylands Smithy can be found on the ancient Ridgeway, on the Oxfordshire/Wiltshire border, not far from the Uffington White Horse hill fort. The whole countryside around Uffington has breathtaking scenery and is a popular area for locals and tourists alike. Waylands itself is an ancient Neolithic burial chamber named after the Saxon god Wayland, a god of smithing and magic. The tomb and surrounding beech trees are fenced off, with a gate to allow entrance to sightseers. It is a very beautiful and tranquil place, and many people seek it out to enjoy its atmosphere for a while.

This story was told to me by a nineteen-year-old young man called Gwynne:

'My girlfriend, Rhiannon, came up from Chepstow to stay with me at my mum and dad's house in Wantage one weekend in August 2002. We fancied some time on our own so we decided to go camping, the weather was good and I love being outdoors.

I wanted to go and stay near to some fishing lakes. I could then do some fishing and Rhiannon could read. She always had her nose in some book or other. Well, Rhiannon had been busy having her nose stuck in a book called *Occult Places in Britain*. She was always seeking out these weird out-of-the-way places and making me take her there. Rhiannon refuses to drive as she once had a psychic reading that warned her of a car accident whilst she was driving. I know it is all piffle but I have never tried to talk her out of it, as I am inclined to think that what you believe you receive.

Anyway, she suggested we go camping at Waylands Smithy. Luckily this place is not a million miles away from where my parents live. When we got there, even I was impressed. It certainly was in a stunning location. We parked the car several hundred yards away from the actual monument; then we carted all our stuff up the Ridgeway track and into the fenced area surrounding the tomb. When we entered the fenced area where the tomb is, Rhiannon ran all around the place in ecstasy. In and out she went, cooing all the way at the wonder of it. I pitched the tent well away from the entrance gate, concealed a little in the privacy of the rather magnificent beech trees that stand all around.

This was about four o'clock on a Friday afternoon. The weather turned out to be glorious. So, after I had erected the tent, we sat around, feeling relaxed in the sunshine. Several different groups of people came to look at the tomb. I was surprised to find that there were so many visitors as the place is quite out of the way but not so Rhiannon, who sagely told me that it was very near to Lammas, which is a pagan festival, or if I'd rather, a witches' sabbat.

That evening, Rhiannon lit some particularly pungent incense in the mouth of the tomb, to placate the gods she had said; after all we were expecting to sleep in a sacred place, and then we went for a walk. We followed the Ridgeway track along, and took in the wonderful countryside. Rolling downs and huge yellow cornfields stretched before us, and we stopped awhile and watched as a monstrous combine harvester cut the golden corn. I was pleasantly surprised when we got back from our walk to find the tent still standing; and that it had not been squatted in by people with rings in their noses, heads, ears, and goodness knows where else. Of course, Rhiannon chided me for such thoughts and said that you should never judge books by their covers.

Soon it got dark, and a full moon rose, buttery and bright in the sky. It was a wonderfully warm night, and Rhiannon and I just lay on the grass on our backs, arms above our heads; gazing at the moon and the myriad of shining stars in the night sky. It was such a tranquil place to be, especially at night, when visitors wane to nothing and you find yourself left completely alone with nature.

At around 11 pm, the relaxing atmosphere and all that fresh air made us feel more than ready for bed. So I got out our sleeping bags, whilst Rhiannon made a last check to see that no cattle had happened to stray our way. She didn't need a torch as the moon was now up high and full, casting its soft glow over the surrounding landscape; silhouetting the night.

We must have gone off to sleep like logs. I can't even remember actually falling asleep, and nor could Rhiannon but I woke with a start and realised that she was shaking my arm. As I came round from sleep, I realised that she had an edge of fear to her voice.

"Gwynne, there is something out there, near to the tomb entrance I think."

"You what?" I felt and sounded grumpy. I hoped it wasn't going to be imaginary cows as it had in so many previous camping trips.

"Gwynne. Please. I heard something."

I sat up and listened. I could not hear anything at all. It did cross my mind that there could be other people out there. So I got out of the tent and walked down the length of the long barrow. I could see Rhiannon peering out at me through the tent flap. I walked along the spine of the tomb, all the way to the huge sarsen stones that stood at its entrance. The night was still and absolutely silent, except for the alarm cry of a cock pheasant I had obviously startled from its roost. There was not even a breath of wind, and it was very warm. There was certainly no one about. And the fence and stile-gate made it quite impossible for any large animals to enter. I began to wonder if perhaps Rhiannon had heard a fox on the prowl. But, strangely enough, I did find myself trying to shake off the idea that there was a kind of expectancy in the air; that perhaps this place did in fact hold some kind of old magic.

I shook myself out of this, cursing Rhiannon for her ability to rub things off on me, and went back to the tent. Rhiannon was still peering through the tent flap nervously.

"Nothing there," I said, boldly. I saw the tension go from her body as I climbed back into the tent. Rhiannon struck a match and lit a little tea light lantern with a scented candle inside.

"Shall we have some hot chocolate?" she asked, opening a flask she had made earlier.

I really didn't want to; I would much rather have gone back to sleep. But I could see that Rhiannon was unsettled; so it was much easier to agree to the chocolate. As we sat, cross-legged, with our mugs of chocolate, I asked her what it was she thought she had heard.

"I really did hear something, Gwynne." Her eyes were huge and round.

"Yes?"

"I heard a horse."

I almost spat out a mouthful of chocolate in amazement, and amusement, "A horse?"

"Yes. A horse." Her face was deadly serious in the candle light.

I put my arm around her.

"Look petal. There are no horses in the fields around here. You saw that for yourself. And anyway, a horse certainly would not be able to get in here, it is fenced off, and no way could a horse walk through the stile-gate, a horse is a wide creature!"

She looked very troubled for a while. Then her face relaxed, and she said, "Of course you are right Gwynne." Then she sighed.

"Perhaps you were dreaming, love?" I offered in explanation.

"No. I know I was not dreaming. I had been awake some time before I heard it. It was the sort of snorting noise that horses make when they blow down through their noses… Gwynne…"

"Yes?"

"When you were getting the sleeping bags ready I went down into the mouth of the tomb …"

"You did?" I wondered what she was about to say next.

"Yes I did."

"And?"

"I saw that people had put flowers in there. Field poppies, and stalks of corn with the grain head still on."

"Yes I saw that too."

"And candles. And coins."

"Coins?" I asked, a little puzzled.

"Yes. Mainly silver."

"Oh," was all that I could think of to say.

"Why do you think they put in coins, Gwynne?"

"I have no idea. Perhaps it is the same thing as people putting money into a wishing well? You know, to bring good luck or whatever."

"Oh, is that it? Oh good. You see I put a coin in there too, Gwynne."

"Well, that was nice." I just wanted her to settle back down enough to go back to sleep. Rhiannon was always full of nervous energy at the best of times; and I feared that she might be awake all night now her imagination had been fired.

But to my surprise she let out a sigh that ended in a yawn, and clambered back into her sleeping bag, after finishing her chocolate. I looked at my watch as I gratefully climbed into my own sleeping bag; it said 12.30 am.

"Gwynne …"

"Yes?"

"Gwynne I like it here. Even if it is a bit strange."

"Yeah. Me too."

It seemed a very short time after this, but it was in fact about an hour, when I felt Rhiannon's long fingers digging into my arm again. "Gwynne!" she whispered urgently.

"What the …?" I was finding it hard to wake properly from the deep slumber I had gone back into.

"Gwynne. Please. Come out here!" Rhiannon was now outside the tent. "Don't move quickly, or make too much noise or anything Gwynne." I could tell by her hoarse whisper that her mouth had gone very dry, so I wasn't quite sure what would meet my eyes as I emerged from the tent.

I stumbled out, rubbing the sleep from my eyes with my fists. When I could eventually focus properly again, I could make out in the moonlight what looked like a grey horse. It was a horse of noble bearing and equine beauty, with arched neck and long flowing mane and tail. And standing next to it, steadying it with bridle in hand, was a tall slender woman, with fair hair that fell to her waist. She had on some kind of long gown with a cloak throw over it. They were stood at the entrance to the tomb, woman and horse together. I could see them very clearly in the soft moonlight.

I just stood there staring at them in disbelief. The spell was broken by the fact that Rhiannon's nails had dug into the palm of my hand as she was holding it so tightly. When I turned again to look at the woman and the horse, they were gone. They had vanished into thin air!

Without waiting I ran to the tomb entrance. I looked everywhere around. But there was no sign of woman, or horse. I ran through the stile-gate and even down the Ridgeway track to where we had parked the car, the chalk path standing out white in the moonlight. But there was nothing to be seen anywhere of the woman or the horse.

I ran back to the tent. Rhiannon was stood outside, a fleece blanket wrapped around her. She was shivering despite the warmth of the night. I lit the lamp quickly, then fired up the gas stove and put the kettle on it. For all of this time neither of us said a word to each other.

It was only when we were safely back inside the tent with steaming mugs of tea that Rhiannon ventured to speak. "Did you see her?"

I squirmed and fidgeted before answering. "I really don't know what it is I did see, Rhiannon."

"Yes you do!" she had become haughty and cross at this. "You saw **her** with **her** horse." She said the 'her' like she knew who the 'her' was.

I was stumped now. I thought that I could explain what I had seen by believing it was because I was half asleep. But Rhiannon had seen the exact same thing!

"I think I did see something like that," was all that I would shamefully admit. I did not feel happy about saying it, I didn't want to get caught up in Rhiannon's hocus-pocus. Besides, there was no rational explanation. I like to have a rational explanation for everything. I also didn't like the uncanny feeling that I had experienced whilst looking at the woman and the horse. It made me think of the stories my gran used to tell us back in

Wales as kids. Stories that made your skin prickle and check under your bed before you went to sleep at night.

Rhiannon could tell my mood so she sulkily finished her tea and got back into her sleeping bag. I blew out the lamp and did the same. We both pretended that we had gone back to sleep, but really we had a lousy night. I also thought I heard Rhiannon let out some little sobs. I felt like a real pig because I would not admit to seeing the woman and the horse.

The next morning, Rhiannon, with red rimmed eyes, demanded to be taken back home to Chepstow. I did not argue with her, but quietly packed up all of our things ready to go. On our way out, at the tomb entrance, I slyly scanned the ground for any signs of hoof prints. It was dry and dusty; and there were none. We spoke very little on our way back to Wales. Then, as we neared the Severn Bridge, Rhiannon said, "I don't know if I want to see you again." She was crying.

"Christ!" I punched the steering wheel. "I won't join in with seeing the bloody ghost, or whatever it was, and you want to dump me!"

We were silent again after that. When I pulled up outside her parents' house, I turned to her and said, " I did see them, Rhiannon. The woman and the horse. I know that we both did. But I don't know what they were. We saw them; then they just vanished. Just vanished."

"Yes, they vanished." She turned and kissed me. Tears were still trickling down her cheeks as she got out and retrieved her things from the boot. She held my hand through the open car window, and bent and kissed me again. "I am so glad that you came clean that you saw them, Gwynne."

I shrugged my shoulders. "Maybe trick of the light ...?"

"Ha! I think not." She smiled a wan smile. "I'll phone you tomorrow."

On the Monday after that weekend I had an email from Rhiannon. It contained a link about Waylands Smithy. I clicked on to it. I scanned through the usual facts about the history and date of the burial chamber, and what was found in it. Then my eye caught a section on the legends about the place, which read: "Wayland was a Saxon god of metal working, enchantment and magic, sometimes also known as Volund. He was thought to be more of the Elven race by some. It is said that, even to this day, if anyone should throw a coin into the tomb and bring a horse that needs shoeing, it will be shod by morning. Sometimes the horse will have been shod with shoes of pure silver."

23

The Chilling Presence on the Flinty Track

This is a story told to me by a young couple called Nigel and Fiona who lived in the Penhill area of Swindon. These incidents happened between 2005 and 2006. Nigel began:

'We would maybe never have experienced what happened had it not been for the fact that we acquired a dog. To start from the beginning, we had our first baby, and I became a house-husband which allowed my girlfriend to continue with her career whilst I looked after our baby boy. And, because someone would now be home most of the day, we decided that it would be nice to have a dog. So we found George, a basset hound who had been through a hard time and gone into Basset Rescue. He was a splendid red and white boy, a gentle giant, a great big sensitive thing on very short legs. We all adored him immediately.

Fiona and I had bought a house together in Penhill so that she only had a little distance to travel to work in Old Town. Despite this, she still needed the car as often she had to travel farther afield with her work. So this left me, baby Jack and, of course, George, with only shanks's pony to get about. Luckily I did not mind this at all as I always find walking a pleasure; besides we could not possibly have financed another vehicle.

Well, George needed plenty of exercise, and baby Jack loved the fresh air, and would gaze dreamily out at the trees, flowers and clouds at the slightest opportunity; which led us to explore all of the walks that we could around us. And, on the days when the car was ours, we explored even farther afield; Jack gurgling in his pushchair and George forever trotting at our side.

During the lovely days of summer we enjoyed ourselves immensely; we often took along delicious picnic lunches. People of all ages would come and talk to Jack and George, and even to me sometimes! But when the days shortened and grew colder I realised that our walks might have to become a little shorter, too. So I set out to find a convenient little route that would not become too muddy with the winter rains, and that was easily attainable from where we were living. I knew that at weekends, with Fiona to look after Jack, I would be able to take George on more satisfying walks.

Eventually Jack, George and I stumbled upon a track which led alongside a small industrial estate not far from Marston Avenue in Penhill. It was an old dirt track with no tarmac, littered with flinty stones, but not too bad for walking on, or pushing the pushchair. It was quite a pleasant walk, despite the small industrial estate, as it was lined with elderly and handsome trees, and some gnarled elder and hawthorn bushes. So Jack still had a chance to look around, and to squeal with delight at a pinking blackbird. And George could safely trot along without his lead. It wasn't perfect with the industrial estate so near by; but it gave us all a chance to get out in the fresh air and stretch our legs.

One cold afternoon in early November, after some rather heavy rainfall, I decided that the track would be the driest and easiest place for us to go for our walk. So I dressed Jack up warmly, and tucked him in his fleecy blanket in his pushchair, put George on his lead and we were off! We followed the track up about half a mile to its conclusion, where we always turned around and walked back homewards.

As usual, Jack was chattering away in some language only known to himself and, curiously, often to George, too. I was chattering away too, telling Jack that when we got home we would make mummy a nice roast dinner. George was some way behind, sniffing at messages left by other dogs, or perhaps at the smell of a fox that had passed by. Then, I don't really know if I just felt that there was someone trying to pass us on the track. You know, the way you can feel that kind of thing when you are out walking, the feeling that someone is behind you, and they usually are. In fact, I thought that I heard the whiz of bicycle wheels and feet on the pedals, but I really could not be sure. Anyway, naturally I pushed the pushchair into the side to let the cyclist by, as the track was quite narrow. But when I had done this and turned around to look, there was no one there! But, strangely enough, George, who is not fond of bicycles, ran off ahead barking as though something had passed by. I found this a bit unnerving at first, but I soon shrugged it off. I rationalised that my believing there to be someone behind us, and pulling the pushchair over to let them pass, had given George all of the signals and body language to suggest that we were being overtaken; hence his running ahead and barking. We walked the track several times after this, but nothing untoward happened at all. I began to think myself fanciful; and laughed at the very thought, as I am a very down-to-earth kind of person.

Then, in the first week of December in that same year, I came down with a heavy cold, which poor little Jack contracted too. So we were unable to take George out for his walks for a couple of days. We did have a large garden luckily, but George loved his walks and missed them terribly. He sat about the house with such a hangdog expression that Fiona could not stand to see it any more, and volunteered to walk him when she got home from work.

That evening Fiona got George on his lead ready to go. I wasn't entirely happy about this as it was very dark outside. But Fiona is a determined girl, and George is more than persuasive with his big, brown, soulful basset eyes, and the way that his ears can literally drip off his head in sorrow. Fiona got her coat and wellies on, took her torch and went off, their destination being the 'Flinty Track' as we had come to call it.

What happened next I was certainly not ready for. Fiona had only been gone about twenty minutes when I heard the front door open, then slam shut. I could hear sobbing coming from the hallway. I rushed in to find Fiona sitting upon the bottom stair trembling and crying. George was standing looking up into her face, as if trying to calm her, his big periscope tail waving gently.

I ran to her and put my arms about her, hardly able to speak. Jack, luckily, had dozed off on the sofa and had not witnessed his mother's distress. I felt sick to the stomach. I was almost afraid to ask what was wrong. I feared that Fiona had been attacked. I felt suddenly so guilty at ever letting her go out in the dark alone. Eventually she calmed down enough to speak.

"I was ever so afraid, Nigel."

I was appalled. I asked if she had been attacked, and if I should call the police.

But she said, "No. No!" and just sat on the stairs where she was, white and trembling.

I could think of nothing else to do, so I got some Bach Rescue Remedy, put some drops in water and gave it to her to sip. I tried to get her to move to the sitting room where she would be more comfortable, but she said that her legs felt far too weak to move. So then I went and poured her a small Cognac, and as she drank it I could see her relax a little, and that she was slowly gaining the ability to speak about her ordeal.

"Can you actually tell me what happened now?" I asked her gently.

"Well …" she took a deep breath that ended with a little sob and continued, "I went a little way down the Flinty Track, when suddenly, and for no apparent reason, I just felt very afraid and started coming back.

George didn't seem at ease either. His tail wasn't up and he kept on shying at something rather like a horse; and to be honest this spooked me up even more. The track was very, very dark, I shone the torch around but couldn't see anything or anyone, but something just didn't feel right …"

I nodded, refilled her glass, and went and sat alongside her on the bottom stair as she continued again. "I put George on his lead and shone the torch around again but there was nothing to be seen. Nothing at all, save for the trees. But I had this dreadful feeling that … that something was behind me. I mean I did not hear anything. I could see nothing but the feeling remained, something was behind me. Oh, it still makes the hairs on the back of my neck prickle to think of it!" She stopped and gulped the Cognac down. "So I hurried homewards. But …", she faltered, stammering out the words in her distress. "But … but as I came nearly to the end of the track, in the homewards direction, I heard something behind … It sounded just like someone riding a bicycle behind me. I could hear their breathing too … Oh my God! Then, I felt this icy draught and I instinctively moved aside. I think I let out a little scream … But nothing passed me, Nigel! No one passed by! And then, and then, it was as if George could actually see it, whatever it was and he leapt at it like he does when someone rides a bike past us … Oh my God, Nigel. What do you think it was? Do you believe in ghosts?"

I stood up quickly. "No I don't believe in ghosts. Never have." I said. I did not know what to think truthfully, but she was in such a nervous state that I was afraid I might aggravate it if I encouraged stuff about the supernatural. Although, I did think of my own experience down the Flinty Track, I didn't want her to get into a state as she had been quite stressed of late with her job, which was very demanding. So I played the whole thing down, whilst assuring her that I believed what had happened, but somewhere there would be a rational explanation.

Fiona talked of this experience for some time. But eventually she said little more about it; except that she had told a work colleague about it who said that supernatural experiences were far more common than a lot of people believe; she had even had one herself. I still played it all down, even when she told me this. I didn't want us all to end up being afraid of our own shadows as it were.

Then we both let it slip from our memories really. It was pushed to the back of our minds as Christmas approached; and we both delighted in Jack's wonder at the tree and all the sparkling decorations. We had a lovely, if busy, time, with friends and family visiting; and everything seemed too warm and solid and real to think about the things that had happened down the Flinty Track. But we did not walk George down there again. Although we did not speak of it, we avoided the Flinty Track.

Then, as winter melted into spring, and the tender sticky buds of the horse chestnut trees were appearing, I boldly decided to take Jack and George down the Flinty Track again. I think it was really to prove to myself that it really was just an ordinary track, and that we must not let our imaginations run riot.

It was a glorious day, the sky a cobalt blue. A very clear day, a day where the bright sunshine shone into every nook and cranny, and left no shadowy places for you to see spooks where there weren't any. I felt light and happy as I walked, the warm sun welcome on my skin. Jack crowed in his pushchair and George positively galloped along, seeming to be glad to be back on some old territory.

We did the usual, walking up to the top of the track, then turning for home. We met a couple of people on the way. One was an elderly lady, with a little Yorkshire terrier that snarled and barked at George; this had rather the same effect as a mouse might have if it tried to boss an elephant, that is, George ran from it! And, the other was a middle-aged man leisurely riding a rather antique-looking bike.

We were all in good spirits and I stopped on the way back homewards to give Jack a Farley's rusk as he was demanding food. I was just bent over the pushchair doing this when I heard a bicycle behind. Thinking it was the man on the antique bike, I pulled over and clipped George on his lead as he always took offence if bicycles came from behind us.

I felt an icy blast and heard the whiz of wheels. But no one was passing us at all! Well, no one that I could see anyway. George barked and nearly tugged me over. Jack was startled and started to cry. It was then that I realised for sure that a phantom cyclist rides along the Flinty Track.

Index